Willie Whisky

by

Ken Grant

The Life And Times Of Willie Whisky

KEN GRANT

www.kengrantbooks.co.uk

This Book was published by Ken Grant Books, 2007.

First Edition.

Designed, typeset, printed, and bound completely in-house
By BrightSpark Publishing,
Unit 11
The Wards
New Elgin
ELGIN
IV30 6AA

Telephone 01343 544336
Or mobile 07967 178224

CHAPTER ONE

HAME O' THE CRATUR

1

Long gone are the days when you could leave school at fifteen and get a job in your local distillery - but for Dufftown lad Willie Thompson a job at Glen Dufftown Distillery was there if he wanted it. Born just after the Second World War, in The Stephen Memorial Hospital, Dufftown, to John and Mary Thompson, Willie was in the heart of whisky country. With seven distilleries within the town boundary, Dufftown - for any whisky connoisseur - was the Holy Grail: 'the' whisky capital of the world. As the very old rhyme goes, 'Rome was built on seven hills, Dufftown was built on seven stills'.

Dufftown nestles neatly in amongst the Conval hills, with the town of Keith on one side, Aberlour on the other, and approximately twenty miles inland from Elgin - which is situated on the main artery, the A96, halfway between Aberdeen and Inverness in the North East of Scotland.

Willie's dad, John Thompson, was the brewer at Glen Dufftown. He was sure that the world of whisky would seep into young Willie's brain so much that he'd consider taking the vacant job with the warehouse staff at Glen Dufftown when he left the school. It would be a long climb up the whisky ranks to managerial level, but they say the best distillery managers all started their careers wearing dungarees.

In a small town with a total population of fifteen hundred, and whisky distilling the main industry, it was not surprising to find more than one family member on a distillery staff. Willie's older sister, Liz, worked in the bottling hall at Glen Dufftown, while his mum cleaned the offices each day from 5pm to 7pm; Willie's grandfather retired as manager of Ben Conval Distillery; his uncle Sandy was a maltman at Glen Auchtie; and two of his older cousins were trainee still men at Glen Kinvie and Ben Venie.

Willie himself pulled on his first pair of distillery dungarees after close season 1960. (Close season? Simply, that's the distillery world's term for closing down production, so that annual maintenance of the distilleries could take place.) Steel toe capped boots, along with hard wearing gloves - akin to a welder's - and a canvas apron, all supplied by the company, was the trademark uniform of the distillery warehouseman. A whole world away from Willie's school clothes, but he soon broke them in over the first couple of weeks.

2

With Dufftown boasting seven distilleries, Rothes not far behind with five, Keith having three, and outlying communities within a thirty mile radius having at least one distillery on their doorstep, Willie often wondered how many gallons of whisky it all equated to per head of population.

"Well, Willie", his granddad would say, "When old distillery workers coonted their money, they would say, 'gallons, shillings, and pence'.

When this homily sailed over Willie's head, his granddad explained: "You see, Willie, makin' whisky is nae rocket science - although some o' the stuff these days tastes like rocket fuel! They've tampered too much wi' the cratur, and the quality has suffered. But mind you, despite 'a the tamperin' it's still worth pinchin'! Some still boys dogs are niver empty. But jist min' the Golden Rule, Willie - if you're gonna' pinch whisky, dinna get caught!"

After laughing himself hoarse, Willie's granddad continued:

"Of course you can aiyways mak yer ane. Ah them smoke plumes in the Cabrach are nae jist fae hooses, ye ken. Aye, ye'll dee a'right at the whisky, Willie. You'll surprise yoursel' wi' just how high you can fly if you participate in the water of life."

3

Willie had always been inquisitive. Long before pub quiz nights were invented he had lots of fun making up silly questions for his work mates to answer. His sense of humour had been popular at school, and now he was grafting at the whisky he was proving to be a hit with his workmates, relieving the boredom of rolling barrels every day.

Some of Willie's questions bordered on the ridiculous, mind, but at least he was having a stab at humour. The line that always infuriated his mum was when she would ask him if he'd changed his socks. His stock, (or should that be 'sock') answer was always: "Yes, I've changed the one on the left foot with the one on the right foot!"

"Did 'DUNG'arees get their name because farmers were the first group of workers to wear them?" always seemed to elicit a good laugh.

Favourite questions from Willie, to win yourself a double Mortlach, were:

"Name Dufftowns' seven distilleries."

"What is the date of the Dufftown boys ball?"

"What year old is Ben Venies best dram?"

"Where in Dufftown is the Glen Dufftown Restaurant?"

"Which Dufftown chip shop serves the smallest ice cream?"

"Which way do the flags fly on Fred's flag poles?"

4

Yes, all in all Willie enjoyed a laugh. But his passion in life was football. He'd played for his school teams from primary through secondary, and captained the Banffshire under fifteen select in a North of Scotland schools' tournament. In his last few months at school, Willie was asked if he'd like a game in the Speyside Welfare league, and he decided he'd like to play for the 'Stills'.

The league was made up of teams from Aberlour, Rothes, Tomintoul, Keith and Dufftown. The last mentioned had two teams: Dufftown FC, and the aforementioned The Stills.

In his second season, Willie was the league's top scorer, making highland league club scouts come to watch him, inundating him with offers to come along to team training nights. But Willie would always refuse - without giving any real reason why. He did accept a trophy from the welfare league for being top scorer, but every one at the club wondered if he'd ever delight in telling his grandchildren some day what the trophy was for.

5

Since Willie was ten years old he regularly attended Glenlivet piping school, joining Dufftown pipe band on his fourteenth birthday. The highlight of the year for him and the band was always the town's highland games, when afterwards they seemed to unofficially have the freedom of Dufftown.

Growing up in Dufftown among the Conval Hills and lower reaches of the Cabrach, the winters would stretch themselves out so close to summer there would appear to be no Spring. After a heavy fall of snow, Willie and friends would sledge from the top of Conval Street all the way down to the Cabrach Road entrance. That run must've been the longest sledge run in Banffshire.

The other great winter's night pastime in Dufftown was 'rumblin' spoots'. For those who don't know the technique, pay attention: you take a sheet of old Northern Scot, P and J - or even a page of the Dufftown News - stuff it loosely up somebody's down pipe, and light the end! The result, if it's successful, is a rumblin' spoot. But as cast iron piping gave way to plastic guttering and down pipes the game gave way to less hazardous pastimes on the streets of

Dufftown. Legend has it that Willie was a gifted rumbling spooter in his day.

6

If Willie's ambition was to reach the dizzy heights of distillery management, he certainly did not make the best impression during the first few weeks in his new job. Racing through the cindered distillery yard on his trusted three speed Raleigh bike, nearly crashing into the distillery tractor and barrel trailer head on, and struggling to make the barrel store for the eight am start wasn't going to endear him to the higher echelons of the firm.

The barrel store wood burning stove - which was lit each morning by the self appointed barrel store foreman - was very much appreciated in the winter months by the lads for five or ten minutes before starting work. But wi' Willie always bein' latchy he never got the benefit of it. At lunchtimes, the out of towners would sit round the stove, eating their daily sandwiches and talking shop.

On whisky filling days, the first job was to mark the barrels with copper stencils of numbers and letters made by the local coppersmith - probably Forsyth's, Rothes. A dab of white paint embossed the distillery name, year of the filling, and cask number on the cask end. The casks filled consisted of Butts, Puncheons, Hogsheads and barrels. Barrels were the smallest at 40 to 45 galls. Hogsheads at 60 to 70 galls. Puncheons and Butts held around 100 to 120 galls. Depending on the quantity of the filling usually determined who the customer was.

Willie's first job was bunging the casks and rolling them onto the barrel trailer for storage in the warehouse.

Soft bunging was a simple enough task with a cork bung and piece of sacking, but the hard bunging which took place once the whisky was matured and due to leave the warehouse was a little more skilful. This involved an oak bung being hammered into the cask and flushed off with an etch.

7

The distillery had just taken ownership of their spanking new red Massy Ferguson tractor. In the days before the war, distilleries kept horses for pulling the barrel trailer, and it also had been known for oxen to have been used. Warehouse staff took turn to look after the horses' welfare.

Filling whisky into barrel sized casks made transporting them to the warehouses easier for the men than the bigger sizes. They were more manageable, too, in the racks, where they would sit maturing for the next five to eight years. The matured whisky would then be hard bunged, loaded into an artic lorry and dispatched for the central belt.

By month two Willie had the barrel rolling down to a fine art. Sometimes, to relieve the monotony of the job, the warehousemen would practice their craft of up-ending empty butts on the cemented filling store floor, using only a foot to propel the cask. The shape of the butt allowed you to give it that extra foot shove for it to swivel on its belly. And if you'd done it right, it would swivel onto its end. Hogsheads were easy, but butts took a lot of know-how.

Like all workmates do when a new start arrives, Willie's peers at Glen Dufftown, wanted to know all about him.

"What's your name?"

"Where do you come from?"

"Do you bide in Dufftown?"

The usual questions - which resulted in the usual answers.

"I'm Willie Thompson fae the Cabrach, but I bide in Dufftown noo, in Knockator Road"

"Och, aye! You're ane o' Jock Thompson's bairns!" To which another work mate added, "We're ah Jock Thompson's bairns! Which one are you?"

"You boys should be on the stage," replied Willie. "It leaves at noon!" Willie's wit made them step back, but they were so glad he had a sense of humour.

"Do you nae play the pipes in the plumber's band - I mean the Dufftown band?"

"Aye, I do. I joined the band last year."

"Hey Willie, did you hear aboot the octopus fa went to bagpipe lessons wi' his pal?"

"No," smiles Willie.

"The class is busy playing away but the octopus is still wrestling with his set of pipes. 'What's the octopus doin?' the instructor asks the octopus's pal. 'It's okay - he'll play them in a minute when he finds out he canna make love to them!' "

With work mates that liked a good laugh, and sales of Glen Dufftown on the increase, there seemed no reason for Willie's future to be anything else but rosy.

8

As the months passed, Willie graduated to the sampling team. This team was usually made up of three guys: one to dip the cask, the second to hold the sampling glass beaker, and the third was the look out. Willie's first undercover mission was a bit nerve racking for the rookie, but come his third one he knew the procedure like a seasoned pro.

There was an unwritten clause in the distillery world rulebook which allowed matured whisky to be taken out of the warehouse for the staff drams. Excise men turned a blind eye once a week to this perk of the job. While the week's supply was being extracted, the excise man would stay in his office in the filling store, and the excise watchman would be sent on an errand to the farthest away warehouse to check the locks, with the instruction that he not return till the samplers had enough golden nectar safely in the brewers office cupboard.

This was a tradition handed down through distillery folklore and each new excise man's credentials were closely scrutinized to make sure there would be no encounters of the wrong kind.

9

Gradually, Willie was getting to grips with his distillery career, being offered overtime on the weekend cleaning shift. Regular weekly cleaning of the mash tun and spirit stills was one of the key factors in keeping the spirit's high quality.

A squad of four men embarked on the cleaning at around two o'clock on Saturday afternoons. Two of the personnel climbed into the mash tun to sweep out the remaining mash, lift the heavy stainless steel plates, and hose it down until spotless, while the other two guys cleaned the spirit stills.

The spirit stills themselves were cleaned with a caustic soda solution and a wire brush. Hot hard work that none of the operators enjoyed. Mash tun cleaning was the more favoured job, but a still man's hourly rate of pay reflected the difference in the two disciplines. When the cleaning was finished you could visit the brewer's office if you so wished to exercise your own... quality control!

Willie, however, just relished the extra pay, as his social life was beginning to expand, for Rock 'n' Roll was filtering through to Speyside, as beat groups started playing the local village halls.

While Willie was learning to play the bagpipes, his pals were learning to play guitar and the drums, and seemingly overnight had formed a beat group with their first gig in the Fleming Hall, Aberlour. The up country-dance scene was in full swing with rock bands appearing every weekend at different venues: Carron Hall, Edinvillie, Aberlour, the Craig, Dufftown, Keith and the Grant Hall, Rothes were all on the circuit.

Funnily enough, none of the bands that played the circuit were called 'The Distillers' - or, indeed, had any name relating to whisky. A missed opportunity, one would think, although the 'Jacobeats' enjoyed a healthy following in the highlands, long before 'Runrig' burst onto the scene.

10

Once a month, for a change - because it is as good as a rest, after all - Willie and a couple of his pals would visit the Bright Lights of the big city: Elgin, that is! For its music scene and nightlife was just that bit more exotic and sophisticated than... Dufftown!

They would take a bus from Dufftown square, and get off off right outside the 'Pot Still' bar on Elgin's High Street. For Speyside whisky men it was a veritable argosy of whisky wonders, with its own full size copper still (not working, of course!) and distillery related art effects. Year upon year, literally thousands of tourists, and whisky lovers from all over the world, visit Dufftown, and quaff copious quantities of the cratur in its pubs, but none equalled the 'Pot Still'.

Today, thirty five years on, there is still no bar on Speyside that can match the late and lamented 'Pot Still' as it used to be. For, unfortunately, the 'Pot Still' became a shoe shop in the late seventies. This, coincidentally, was also the fate of the 'Stag' bar in Commerce Street (which raises the question 'had all the Elgin people suddenly grown two extra feet ?').

Other bars from Willie's heyday that live on in 'spirit' only are the 'Crown' in Batchen Street and the High Street; the 'City'; the 'Carousel'; the 'Tower'; the 'El Cid'; and the 'La Dolce Vita'.

Although new bars have sprung up, there still remains a few from the sixties and seventies that remind Willie of his social visits to Elgin.

After a round of the bars, and a fish supper from the Northern chip shop, the threesome would make their way east along the High Street to dance the night away at the 'Two Red Shoes' ballroom.

Synonymous with the Elgin dance scene, the 'Two Red Shoes' saw a host of famous sixties' bands strut their boogie stuff on its stage - none more famous than 'The Beatles'! On the Fab Four's Scottish tour in June '63 they had played Buckie, Dingwall, Banff, and, of course, Elgin

- but, unfortunately, they had been caught in snow and didn't make it to their Keith gig at St Thomas's Hall.

11

Snow! That frosty precipitation was something that Speyside distilleries knew all about - in fact, each distillery from the largest to the smallest had their very own snowplough. It was, after all, essential that the whisky kept flowing.

The distillery road ends were specially tended too, after the council snowplough had passed, for deliveries of barley, yeast, caustic soda, and a supply of barrels from local cooperage were arriving daily. While tradesmen - the likes of coppersmiths, electricians, plumbers, brickies, joiners and roofers - were in regular employment at most distilleries throughout the boom years of the '60s and '70s.

The more tradesmen there were, the more whisky that was needed for the complimentary drams. Sampling teams became more slick and slight of hand as the cliche 'supply and demand' kicked in.

Surrounded by thousands and thousands of gallons of whisky, in shades of golden brown to black, the temptation for some of the tradesmen was understandably overwhelming. Even the daily allocation of three drams a day - morning, lunchtime, and 5pm - was not sufficient to satisfy their taste buds.

The 'Daily Drams' was a hundred year old tradition that came to an end in the mid to late 1970s. Its demise was initiated by Speyside doctors as so many of their patients (not only distillery workers) entered their surgeries (if they could find the door!) with alcohol related problems.

12

Distilleries, depending on their size, would employ around thirty to forty staff in the various skills needed to produce the cratur. But as automation arrived, fewer personnel were needed, which meant that the distillery companies' profits grew considerably.

As their coffers grew, it was thought that they could easily afford to lose a few gallons to smuggling. Many ingenious ways of getting the spirit out of the warehouses, under the noses of the excise men and watchers were dreamed up. The most essential piece of kit for the warehouse smuggler was a length of rubber hose about two foot long, used for siphoning spirit from the cask into whatever receptacle the smuggler was carrying. Others preferred the slim copper dog lowered gently into the cask, to be retrieved by its attached cord. Spillage was never a problem, as evaporation occurred almost immediately!

Most plans and schemes to extract whisky were usually foiled early on in the quest, but one such tradesman who enjoyed his tipple has now gone down in Speyside folklore for his whisky acquiring skills. While most smugglers took the whisky out the warehouse door in copper 'dogs' or breastplate flasks, the legendary 'spirit spiriter' took his haul out via the warehouse roof!

This was indeed a roofer who had bigger balls than King Kong! He had surrepticiously made up a section of roof which he could remove and lower himself through to be in amongst some of the oldest and best sherry casks at the distillery. Each morning he arrived for work with a five gallon plastic water container (half empty of course). When he loaded this water container back onto his firm's truck at

5pm each day it was still half full - but the fluid now the golden hue of whisky. The roofing job at the distillery was a six month contract - and that's a LOT of whisky!

Good thing don't last forever, and one sunny day on the roof, after one dram too many, he fell asleep... and his time was up. When the police raided his house, his co conSPIRITors were flushing buckets of thirty five-year-old nectar down the toilet drain. It must have looked like prohibition on Speyside. Had he been better organized with his storage facilities, he probably would still be enjoying his booty today.

Another favourite clear whisky (clearic) extraction story was the warehouseman who filled two lemonade bottles and hung them with a length of string round his neck and always left the warehouse wearing a bulky jacket. In the privacy of the filling house barrel store, he would empty the contents of the bottles into his thermos flask, and milk bottle, and carry them undetected in his piece bag past the prying eyes of the excise man and his watcher. Then at the weekend he topped up a sherry whisky cask he had buried in a nearby peat moss.

Ingenious - West coast malt from Speyside!

In the older built warehouses of the '60s and '70s, the casks sat on wooden rails like tram lines with a cinder floor throughout, and if there was a particularly good barrel which had had more attention than it should have, then the loss was simply blamed on leakage and the angels' share. Thus resulting in thousands of drams on speyside being drunk every year free.

A perk of the job that perked you up.

CHAPTER TWO

GOALS GIRLS GILLS

1

In autumn '62, on his 17th birthday, Willie was given his provisional driving licence from his parents. To have a full driving license in the distillery industry would add a string to Willie's bow.

The nearest driving school for lessons was with Srathisla Driving School in Keith. Jimmy Ten Jobs (as he was affectionately known) had a shop in Mid Street, and also a full time job. How did he manage it? As if breathing alone wasn't a hard enough job: every time you saw Jimmy he had a fag in his mouth. Thankfully neither the stress nor the smoking has killed him yet.

Willie enjoyed the lessons: Start engine... mirror... signal... hand brake... move off up and down Mid Street... handbrake start... Drum Road... three point turn... Seafield Avenue... reversing into a lane in Land Street.... And so on.

"When I slap the dashboard, I want you to do an emergency stop," said Jimmy Ten Jobs. Willie's reaction was so instantaneous and spot on that Jimmy felt it was time for Willie to try his test.

One month on, with a full licence to his name, Willie checked car prices in the classified ads of the Northern Scot.

2

As the '60's receded, Willie's new weekend playground with his pals took him further up Speyside to Aviemore, which by then had become a magnet for the twenty somethings looking for fun in summer and winter.

Snow has, of course, been falling on hills since time began, but it took untill the '60s to hone in on its potential for bringing skiers to the slopes of the Gairngorms. Aviemore was a new and exciting weekend haunt, built for the entertainment of visitors. Situated less than an hour's drive from the whisky capital, four young lads could rent a chalet for the weekend and party until they fell over.

Aviemore's night life was a few notches up from downtown Dufftown, and was just the place for social adventures. Wille and the rst of the 'Dufftown dudes' thought it was just magic, as every other weekend in summer they pitched tent in the centrally located camp site, within easy walking distance from the heart of the action. Middle of the road rock bands played the Osprey rooms; if they fancied Scottish-Irish traditional there was the Red McGregor; while at the Post House you could hear live, chart and standards music.

A 'Happy Haggis' fish supper on their way back to their tents, then a good night's sleep, and they'd be up at a respectable time to take a trip up the chair lift, have a swim, go skating and karting or just browse round the shops.

Heaven on Earth!

For their Saturday evening meal the lads had an

assortment of eateries to choose from. One of their favourites was 'The Glochanspiel'. Another round of the bars would follow, and then Saturday would conclude with a dance in the Osprey Rooms.

The homeward drive on Sunday after a bar lunch would take them round past Coylumbridge for a pint, then onto Grantown for another, and home to Dufftown, stopping off for a nightcap at 'The Fife'.

And so another great weekend's entertainment came to a close.

3

After the initial rush of adolescent indulgence's, when Willie's football gave way to beer, girls and the dreaded weed, he was feeling he still had something to offer the game, as he was missing the buzz from scoring goals. So nearly two years after his last game, he polished his football boots and joined Aberlour Villa.

Not being match fit, he struggled through his first two games. But his natural touch was still there, which he showed when he found the net early in the first half of his third game. In subsequent games, his touch got sharper, and word soon went round that Willie Thompson was back playing - and scoring goals.

Six months on, and twenty goals to his credit Willie was enjoying his football like he'd never been away. And, like before, local Highland League club Rothes came knocking at his door. This time, Willie was keen, and he didn't have to be asked twice. Shortly after his eighteenth birthday Willie walked onto McKessack Park for the first time. The Highland League season was half way through, and a win in this home game against Lossie would keep Rothes in the top half of the league table.

The step up from welfare league football to Highland League for most players would be pretty daunting, but Willie was a talented player. He was gifted with that rare ability to know exactly where the goalposts were, and at times made goal-scoring look so easy. During the first half he had a couple of near misses, but he knew in himself that he could score to claim a dream home debut. Ten minutes from the restart a reverse pass found Willie on the eighteen yard line. If his first touch was sheer poetry then his second touch was Robert Burns at his best as he half volleyed the ball low and hard into the corner of the net!

Rothes 1- Lossie 0.

The home supporters cheered their new goal hero, prompting more glory to come. With ten minutes of the game left, a driving cross from the left wing connected with the diving Willie's head and the ball nearly burst the Lossie net. The Rothes fans were ecstatic, and the modest Willie soaked up the adulation like water off a ducks back.

'This is easy,' thought Willie, 'All this fuss over me scoring goals? Maybe I should keep doing it - after all, the boys at work do enjoy a good football blether'.

4

Playing for Rothes raised Willie's stature on Speyside, getting his name in Glen Dufftown's news in the 'Decanter', the high gloss drinks industry magazine. He had seen his name in the P and J, Northern Scot, and Dufftown paper countless times, but to see it in ultra gloss alongside such international names as the whisky Glens, Pieroth,

Lindemans, Seagrams, Perno, and Rothchilds etc. - now that was a bit special.

Willie now had the football buzz more than ever. And for the following two seasons he was top scorer with fifteen and twenty eight goals respectively. He'd established himself as a Highland League player, and the top clubs were keen to sign him. Elgin City, Inverness Caley, Deveronvale, Fraserburgh, and Nairn Country, were all chasing his signature. Professional clubs were also showing an interest, but Willie was settled in his job, and knew his future would always be in the whisky industry.

Rothes had done a good job of nurturing their prodigy, and now the time was right to reap the financial rewards. After weeks of negotiation, Willie signed for Elgin City, giving his reasons as 'delighted to join such a progressive club', 'good bunch of lads', 'great respect for the manager and his staff', and 'they play in the same black and white strip as Rothes'. He couldn't be serious for long - that was Willie's charm.

Elgin training was Tuesday and Thursday nights - but if there happened to be a Wednesday night game then Tuesdays training would be on a Monday. The previous Saturday's scoreline would determine how hard the training would be, and how thorough a tactics talk the players would have to endure.

He was twenty-one years of age, with a good job, a car - and playing for a top Highland League club, Willie had no shortage of girlfriends.

Happy at Borough Briggs and at Glen Dufftown, life in Speyside was good.

'Nowhere in this world,' thought Willie, 'could life be any better.'

5

The local dance scene was Willie's hunting ground. And with his high profile, chatting up the girls came easy. He adopted a laid back approach, and the girls more or less did all the chasing.

One particular girl though, who caught his eye at a Carron Hall dance, lived just up the road at Daluiane Terrace. Willie enquired (being confident of her reply), 'Do you need a lift home?'

His confidence proving well founded, the gallant Willie dropped her off at her parents' garden gate after a goodnight kiss, arranging to meet with her at the following Friday nights dance in the Fleming Hall, Aberlour. There would be a big crowd there, as the Aberdeen band 'The Facels' were billed to play.

'The Facels' were one of the most popular bands on the circuit, playing the best of the standards - and always the latest Number One hit in the pop parade. It was a great night, but Willie couldn't stay too late as he had to get up in the morning for football. His team's game on Saturday was at Peterhead - which meant a 10am start from Dufftown.

Willie's first love was football, and he lived for the high of scoring goals. This was a time in his life where he had no room for long term relationships so, after a few months of juggling interests, his Daluiane doll was back on the dance floor with her friends, circling their handbags. Those up country girls maybe didn't know much about the outside world, but they could name every band, and knew the words of all the songs they sang on the hall circuit.

Playing for Elgin City, Willie drifted away from the Speyside social scene, and would stay overnight on a

Saturday (usually after a home game) with a pal who had his own flat in South Street - which was ideal for nights out on the town.

His pal, Jim Grant, worked as a whisky blender with long established Elgin firm Gordon and MacPhail. They had met during Jim's time at Glen Dufftown's in-house laboratory, and shared a sense of humour in the passing.

6

Three years had drifted by since Willie and his Dufftown pals took the tea time bus down to Elgin on a Saturday. Those nights had been great fun, and Willie was keen to visit the old haunts again. These days he could afford a bar supper to start the evening out, so the Laichmoray Hotel or the Torr House would be the first watering hole.

Willie Thompson the socialite, and Jim Grant the more serious minded scientist, blended well in Elgin pubs, meeting up with other like minded twenty somethings at various hostelries. A new circle of friends was emerging, with football celebrity Willie the central figure. Hotel lounge bars were their scene, such as the Sunninghill, Gordon Arms, Braelossie, St Leonards, and the City. Willie liked the Tower - the lager and lime was just to Willie's taste. The pals were either heavy or pale ale drinkers, but at the Tower they usually drank screw tops.

Though the lads had a steak supper earlier, they fancied Chinese to round off the evening. Elgin's one and only Chinese restaurant in the early seventies - 'Eastern Sunrise' - was a mecca for late night lovers of Chinese food. The five foot two owner Jackie Chan, (no, not the actor's dad!) would pack them in, regardless of their degree of drunkenness. Saturday nights were his weekly harvest, and he ensured a quick turnaround on the tables. S.O.E.P.L was Jackie's Saturday night catchphrase: sit, order, eat, pay, leave. You can sit as long as you like the rest of the week, but on Saturday nights it was S.O.E.P.L.!

7

Back at work on Monday, and Willie is blase about his workmates' comments on his second half goal against Forres. He'd intercepted a pass back, on the edge of the box, rounded the keeper, before slotting the ball neatly into the net. The football talk never lasted very long with Willie's work mates, he was happier just keeping the football to training nights, and Saturday games.

Monday was a filling day at the distillery, and as soon as the filling store door was unlocked for the day's filling, wee Bert would make a beeline for the filling head drip pale. A weekend's drips probably accumulated to half a pint or so, and for Bert that was a good start to the week's consumption. Thankfully for his health's sake, he was found another job where he couldn't get his hands on the spirit so easily.

Considering whisky distilleries have been producing the cratur for two hundred years or so, it was only when the sixties arrived that methods of production began to change. Firing boilers with gas and oil took over from the traditional peat and coal, manual technology became more automated with the seventies. In the eighties the computer world was happening, with the industry spending millions of pounds on improving their output, resulting in over production and companies closing down some distilleries by the late eighties. (moth balled was the term used).

Glen Dufftown malt was a big seller, ensuring that Willie and co. were in full production throughout that period. Malt whisky connoisseurs may say Glen Dufftown is maybe not the best dram on the speyside malt's list, but Willie was proud to be getting a foothold in the whisky world, and he was going to take Glen Dufftown to the top.

8

Catering for foreign tourists grew steadily at Speyside distilleries, to the slick tours of today, exposing the spirit of Speyside for every visitor to take home to all corners of the globe.

In today's world there is malt whisky from Japan and India, (the Japanese drink it raw, and the Indians curry it - though whisky is surely hot enough without currying it). But maybe the Scots have been relying on the mysterious image to sell whisky for too long; they may now need a fresh approach. For brain storming there's no better stimulant than whisky, so it shouldn't be too difficult to come up with fresh ideas to change its persona.

As rivalry between the Distillery companies grew, pitching against each other for bus tour operators to bring their passengers to the new reception centres, some clever clogs invented the malt whisky trail. An ingenious idea, as it was the only one in the world. For the participating stills it was an overnight success. The tourist dollar flowed through Speyside, but while the whisky got stronger, the pound got weaker, and the country was thrown into a three day week in 1973.

"There's nothing we can dee aboot it," said Willie, which infuriated his pal Ronnie. Also a Dufftownite, Ronnie was a nationalist who had more backbone than brose on his plate. He had played on the wing for the still's team, where he delivered many of the finer crosses for Willie's better goals. A plumber to trade, he would often be at Glen Dufftown to fix some piping or perform some other plumbing task - and badgering Willie at tea breaks to go with him to Glasgow rock concerts. Willie always made his football the excuse for not going, but the Rolling Stones were playing the Apollo in two weeks, (maybe for the last time), and it was a Sunday night, so Willie had no excuse this time.

"We'll hire a car!" suggested Willie. "We'll pick up Bob, and then zoom doon the A9!"

So at 10am on Sunday morning they set off, planning a lunch stop at Ballanluig services.

9

Approaching Glasgow, not knowing where to go, they just drove, all the while following signs for the city centre. It was late afternoon when they parked up the car and went looking for a Chinese restaurant.

Eventually finding 'Golden Sun', Willie quiped, "I hope it's as good as Elgin's 'Dragon City' - I just love their chow meins, and lemon chicken."

"I've never been to the 'Dragon City'," says Bob. "Ah that rice an' stuff! I just like mince an' tatties." Bob lived in Aberlour and worked as a painter and decorator wi' local firm Sunderland's, and had known Willie and Ronnie since their school days at Keith Grammar. All Speyside children were bused to Keith before Speyside High School was built.

After downing the Golden Sun's culinary delights - which got the thumbs up from all concerned - the boys arrived at the Apollo theatre relaxed and looking forward to a good concert. On the stroke of 8pm the Stones took to the stage and rocked their audience through two hours of classic rock riffs. Unaware of it, the Speyside trio had witnessed one of the last great rock nights at the Apollo. They were part of history and didn't know it.

And still high on rock adrenalin, their journey home wasn't the long drag up the A9 they had envisaged. The big comfortable car was the trump card.

"We have to do this trip again," said an excited Ronnie. "Let's make it a whole weekend next time! Catch a game at Hampden, then a concert, and some night clubbing!"

They all agreed. So, come the next home international at Hampden, the boys would all be there. Six weeks later Rod Stewart was to rock the Apollo the very night of the Scotland- England game. A Scotland fan and football fanatic, Rod would be at Hampden cheering on his heroes from the V.I.P stand.

Getting tickets for the lads might have been an issue but for their pal Ed who lived in Hillhead, the student area of the city. Craigellachie-born Ed was studying accountancy at Glasgow university, and although he was more into rugby than football he was delighted to get tickets for his pals back home. Willie collected the ticket money from Ronnie and Bob, sent a cheque to Ed, and a week later, booked the hire car.

The Glasgow trip was on, and this time they were

staying for two nights in the city. The boys were back in town!

10

With the excitement of their forthcoming trip, their two weeks at work just flew past. Then, managing to wangle off early on the Friday, they were on the road south by 4pm. All going well, that would see them setting out to the bars around nine, with Ed as guide.

"Okay guys, it's the Horsehoe Bar for starters afore we go up the toon."

"Well, that should be lucky," said Bob. "Whaur efter thatt? The Rabbit's Foot?" he joked..The lads were up for a bit of fun, and laughed.

Within a couple of hours they had left a trail of bars in their wake. Next stop en route was the 'clouther vaults', a bar where all the bohemian types hung out: writers, artists, actors, singers... A busy hostelry - but then it was 11pm Friday night in the middle of Glasgow!

As they entered, they thought they heard Dylan's 'Mr Tambourine man' playing on the jukebox.

"It *is* 'Tambourine man' - but it's live!" pointed out Ronnie. Squeezing through the crowd towards the music they caught sight of the singer. A portly silver bearded guy soaking in sweat, thrashing out the song on an old beat up guitar. He looked twice Bob Dylan's age. He was giving it his all, testimony to the quality of the song.

To see a Bob Dylan concert in Glasgow, now that would be special. They amused themselves with the idea, (but fifteen years passed before they got their wish - and another ten rolled by before his legendary concert in Aberdeen).

"Only in Glasgow would you see this," said Ed. "How would he go down at the Masons Arms, or the Royal Oak?" he asked, naming Dufftown's music 'hot spots'.

"He'd sink like a copper dog," said Willie. "Unless he's playin' an accordion he'll nae even get a gig."

It was Ronnie's round, and the mention of the copper dog seemed to unconsciously throw a switch in their minds, as they all ordered Speyside malts: an Aberlour, a Glenfarclas, a Tomnavoulin, and a Tamdhu.

Self appointed group guide Ed suggested finishing off the evening at the Central Hotel, as it was open till the wee small hours. "We'll go clubbing tomorrow night after Rod's concert.Now who wants another dram - and a cigar to match? It's my round."

11

Up in time for brunch, then off to Hampden to experience their first Hampden roar - and what better game to break their ducks than Scotland verses England!

The 'Auld Enemy' were in town seeking revenge after their defeat at Wembly the previous year. What an atmosphere! It seemed like the whole of Glasgow was out in the sunshine to cheer on the Scottish team. This was one of the great Scotland sides, with stars like Dennis Law, Billy Bremner, Kenny Dalglish, Jimmy Johnstone, Archie Gemmill, and Martin Buchan. England were still building a team as most of the '66 World Cup winners had retired from international football.

It was a capacity crowd of around one hundred thousand heaving, screaming human bodies - more people than the Dufftown four had ever seen.

"All this folk, it must be like putting Inverness, Nairn, Forres, Elgin, Rothes, Aberlour, and Dufftown all together," said Willie, tongue in cheek.

"Shut up, Willie, and enjoy the game," came the collective retort.

Four forty five pm, and the dejected England players troop off the field after a three nill hammering, and the Scottish fans are treated to a lap of honour by their heroes.

12

Elated by the win - and what a win on their first Scotland-England game - the boys were positively floating. And their feet didn't touch the ground until their bums had touched the seats in the 'Golden Sun' for a feed before the Rod Stewart concert.

"Aye it's tough at the top," said Bob. "We're munching away here while Rod does a sound check. I know all about sound checks from when I was with the Rolling Stones," he said, turning on his Mick Jagger impersonation, which was always good for a laugh.

Concert time was approaching as they meandered along to the Apollo to hear one of the most distinctive voices in rock music. The band was wonderful, and Rod showed no inhibitions in his performance. Another sensational night at Glasgow's Mecca of rock.

A full concert and two encores later, out into the electric Glasgow air went our Dufftownites ready to party like it was 1999 - only three and a bit decades early. From bar to bar to bar they raced, until finally reaching the Flamingo night club - and were just sober enough to be let in.

Getting to grips with the Glasgow banter seemed easier to comprehend the drunker they became, but the drunker they became the faster the night disappeared until, far too soon, throwing out time was upon them.

Hailing a cab to Ed's Hillhead home, a few hours sleep was on the cards, before their next treat - visiting the 'Barras' on Sunday afternoon. A real treasure trove, and an eye opener for the boys.

What a fantastic city Glasgow was. They'd never seen anything like it, and were sure it would be a magnet for them in future weekends.

But this weekend was coming to an end, and offering their farewells to Ed they headed north. It would be back to work on Monday - warehousing, decorating and plumbing. Auld claes and porridge, as Scottish grannies would say. Back grafting but already dreaming of their next trip down to Glasgow.

CHAPTER THREE

SHARING THE ANGELS SHARE

1

To amuse his family at tea times, Willie always took the lead in starting the conversations at the table. He would ask questions that he hoped would lead to a humorous conclusion. Such as, "Why, when there are so many distilleries on Speyside called Glen-something-or-other, are there very few guys called Glen?"

He'd continue: "It's such a great name it should have been compulsory to name every still Glen... Whatever. Like Pittieviach would be Glenviach; Balvenie would be Glenvenie; Mortlach would be Glenlach, and so on throughout Speyside."

His dad countered with: "No, no, Willie! You canna do that to the Bens and the Straths. Each distillery has to have its own identity." His dad was adamant.

"What about the tourists?" put in Willie. "Would it nae be easier for them?"

When nobody else agreed with this one, he changed his tack. "What about a new distillery for Aberlour then? They could build it on that land next to McPherson's

Transport. Make it a real showpiece for visitors coming into Aberlour from the Craig and Dufftown."

"Your ideas are good Willie," said his dad. "But Aberlour's a toon for fishers. They come to Dufftown for whisky, and go to Aberlour for salmon fae the Spey. It's a different market, Willie."

Being out numbered at the table, he tried another angle:

"The still should employ a piper to play for the visitors. In fact, nae just Glen Dufftown. I could offer my services to all the stills on the malt trail."

"Now you're talkin' some sense, Willie. Go for it! It's a great idea. And when you've made your fortune you could get a personalised number plate on your car."

"Aye, I could. But it would be cheaper changing my name. That's anither guid idea - Glen Thompson! That's a good name for a Scottish piper. Or should I go the whole hog, and call myself Glen McPherson, or McLeod - or better still, Glen Gary McGreger..."

"Stop Willie, you're getting carried away," said his mam, heaping a dollop of porridge onto his plate.

"Ach, awa, woman, " said his dad with a laugh. "It would be a laugh."

"That's it. I'll get a McGreger kilt for pipin' at the stills, and 'Glen Gary McGreger' will be my show time name."

2

Willie's sister Liz had been going out with Dufftown lad Ian Malcolm for the past couple of years, and the ringing of wedding bells would soon be heard through the Conval hills. Conscious not to clash with games day, the couple set a date for the following April.

A spring wedding in Dufftown was a bit risky, weather wise, as it has been known to snow as late as June: not just a shower of hailstones, but a couple of inches of heavy, thick white stuff. Nevertheless, the Thompson family had a celebration to look forward to, and no bad weather would spoil their day.

Liz's fiancé was a cooper at the Dufftown cooperage in Balvenie Street. He, like his future brother in law, went straight to the job from leaving school at fifteen. Making whisky barrels was a very physically demanding and 'stewy' job, with the constant noise of hammering and grinding of the metal hoops that hold the casks together.

Despite its physical demands, the job had one of Speyside's best perks - free whisky. Cradled in the bowels of every emptied cask returned to the cooperage for repair after their stay in the warehouse, there would rest a substantial dram.

Many a cooper fell foul of the amber spirit from the returning casks (known in the whisky world as 'billans' while still at their work. But the majority would take it home, filter it through their wives' nylon stockings several times, and present it as a very palatable dram. Housewives new to Dufftown, would often wonder who the black rubber men were at five o'clock, staggering up Balvenie Street from the cooperage - but long time locals knew they were only coopers who couldn't resist temptation.

Almost literally next door, the Legion club was a handy watering hole for the coopers to gather their thoughts before trudging up the street, home to a cozy roaring coal fire, and plenty of tongue soup.

3

Liz and Ian were giving themselves six months to plan their wedding day, and where else but Mortlach church would be the venue. Their parents had exchanged their vows there in front of one hundred guests, and what was good enough for the goose was good enough for them.

A piper from the Dufftown band would entertain them on arrival at the church, while the wedding photography got underway. The main family pictures, they decided, would be taken at Balvenie Castle - one of Dufftown's most prominent landmarks - while the wedding feast and dance was to be held in the Memorial Hall, but prepared by the staff of the town's Commercial Hotel. Being that both families were from the town, that meant half of Dufftown would be at the dance, and the hotel's function room would be far to small for such a crowd.

Part of the excitement for a young couple getting married is the planning of their big day. From the moment they set the date it's all systems go.

Liz had met Ian at the Dufftown boys' ball (a kind of first footing get together under the one roof) which is always held on January the 2nd - even if the 2nd falls on a Sunday. It's a night where the young male stags of Dufftown 'marked their territory', and cemented their friendships over a few slugs from half bottles of the cratur. Dufftown boys ball traditionally was a black tie evening, with a sprinkling of highland dress.

Gone were the days of rumbling spoots. This was now the era of 'snog a dog'. This was a game among the stags to see who could get a snog with the least attractive girl at the dance. Not a game for the faint hearted, as those who succeeded had to drink a dram, bought by each of his mates. It's the kind of game that quickly depletes the opposition, and completely destroys any chance of a romantic liaison taking place. No romance, but great fun to be part of the Dufftown folklore tradition.

Ian Malcolm though, was a quieter breed of Dufftown male, even leaning towards shyness at times. The kind of guy who would stand in a queue at the bar and never seem to get served. Finding the courage to ask a girl to dance was virtually impossible, but the moment he saw Liz dancing with her friends round an assortment of handbags he knew he would have to muster up the courage from somewhere. Two more drams and he was getting there. Soon he was treading that fine alcohol line between 'enough' and 'don't care, let's hae another dram'.

Getting boozy enough to loosen the tongue, but coherent enough to make sense, the brave Ian crossed no man's land to separate his prey from the pack. And the result was the upcoming wedding!

Ian's mates were never as cautious with their drinking: they were always looking for fun on the edge, drinking hard, playing hard, laughing loud, and telling jokes. They reminded each other about the American visiting Dufftown at new year who, on passing by the Memorial hall on the evening of Jan 2nd and hearing the sound of bagpipes, asked, "What's going on in there?"

"Oh they're just holding the Dufftown boys' ball.

"Holding it?" queried the American. "They must be jumping on it!"

Come midnight they were all absolutely howling... tatties o'er the side... toot a roo... blazin'... blootered... shit marack... guttered... minced... smashed... paralytic... (All good local expressions for being one over the eight!)

4

Willie's dad John was planning his retirement from Glen Dufftown at sixty, after forty five years with the company. He was now fifty five, and wanted to pass on his knowledge, and wealth of experience in the whisky industry, to Willie.

Bob the miller was due to retire during close season, and this would be a chance for Willie to join the production side of making whisky. "Grist to your mill of knowledge, Willie," his dad said.

And so it was that when production resumed that summer, Willie became trainee miller. (rung two on the ladder to managerial status). Milling the grain for mashing was a dusty job, and Willie was eager to get this part of his development over and done with. He had his wish granted six months later when two long serving production staff members accepted retirement packages from the company. Now a mash man, Willie was a lot happier, and could clearly see the career path his dad had set him on leaving school.

Quietly pleased, Willie's dad brought up the subject of golf with him. "Are you goin' to find time for a round on the course?"

"I've nae got time for a round in the pub, far less on a golf course!" Willie replied.

Most distillery managers were golfers, it went with the territory. If you wanted to climb that ladder, you needed to swing (but not with the manager's wife, if you wanted to keep your job). Distillery companies held in-house golf outings as well as sponsoring tournaments, and, for Willie, golf would be a good replacement after he retired from playing football.

Sets of golf clubs cluttered many brewer's and manager's office cupboards when not practicing their swings in the empty malt barns. If you could hit the ball hard enough to rebound off the far wall, that gave you a good indication of how your game was improving. Distilleries with malt barns always produced the best foursome. (you know what I mean!).

The association between whisky and golf was fused way back, and although there are some still managers who don't know a putter from a seven iron, golf is traditionally the older distillery workers' sport. Maybe it's because golf bags have got very good pockets for hiding bottles of whisky, and bottles of whisky are good collateral for paying for rounds of golf, and cases of the nectar are good for paying club memberships. Who needs cash when you have liquid gold?

Many ingenious ways would have been deployed in getting the whisky home without suspicion for family and friends to enjoy. As long as every one of the distillery staff who wanted whisky got their share, life at Speyside distilleries rolled along from mash to mash, distillation to distillation, and filling day to filling day. Sentiments that spun well in the industry, but it was the offbeat stories that made good family conversation in the Thompson household.

With fifty years living on Speyside, John Thompson had heard quite a few. One of his favourites was about a warehouseman who was being consistently too enterprising, causing concern among his peers every time he entered a warehouse. With the aid of two lemonade bottles tied to the straps of an old pair of dungarees and hung round his neck, he successfully smuggled home around five gallons a week. At his own secret private warehouse he had two hoggies (casks): one for clear whisky, one for brown. The good stuff he sold for £5 a bottle (a premium price in the sixties, probably more than the distillery got per bottle).

Hugely suspicious, the management and excise man couldn't catch him red handed, so they hatched a plan, and gave him the delivery van driver's job. When several cases of whisky went missing, and then turned up at local hotels, they knew they had their man. The smugglers career may have come to an end, but his 'hoggies' were never found.

5

Friday evenings in Dufftown were reserved for visiting, with regular callers trudging their way through the snow and rain. Everyone had cars, but this was a weekly pilgrimage between eight and nine pm that had to be made by foot.

Very little was said in conversation during their two hour stay, but they left the house heavily weighed down in each jacket pocket, and with a noticeable stagger. Not so much the angels' share as they weren't quite dead yet, just sad cases who enjoyed whisky as their servant but had let it become their master. For them, every Friday was Christmas - and every Saturday was hogmanay.

6

In the sixties and seventies if you didn't have a direct job in the whisky industry, the next best thing was to supply to it. One of the most successful businessmen to emerge on Speyside was the galvanized pail salesman.

Each distillery needed at least twenty pails, and the smugglers' pail needs (if he was serious) would reach the hundred mark. Rafters in farmers' barns were good places to hang your booty. In out of the way crofts in Glenlivet and the Cabrach you would see row after row of buckets just hanging there. The farmers said it was good for the beef, it gave your steak a sort of pale malty taste. The spirit of Speyside, the local folk will tell you, was in everything and everybody. Spirit fall out, they called it. In such a distillery populated area, the angels share takes forever to reach heaven, and that's why the populous walk around all the time looking so happy.

7

Some of the first tourists to visit the new whisky malt trail centres were Japanese businessmen. Thinking they had found a new angle to make money, they shipped to Japan all the necessary ingredients for making whisky. The process of making whisky is the same the world over, but what gives Scottish whisky its uniqueness is a closely guarded secret - and if you were told what it is, you would have to be likked (Sorry, that's an old theatre joke).

The real truth is nobody knows why Scottish whiskies have their own characteristics. Dufftown's seven distilleries are within half a mile of each other, and are all using the same ingredients and methods of distillation, yet their bouquets and palates are all different .

It would be unethical for those who work for

distillery companies to honestly tell you what their favourite legitimate dram is when their livelihood is at stake. Even if you bought them double malts all night they would just tell you: "Weel, I hid a sook fae a fifty six hoggie ance, which wis pretty good, but I canna mind fit still I wis at." No matter how hard you tried to grill them, they would still give you a non committal answer.

Maybe there is no such a thing as the 'best' whisky, as they are all so good - and deciding between them is a tricky albeit pleasurable job.

8

Willie's dads other pastime when not on the golf course, or tending to his garden was entertaining with his group 'The Palladium rejects' around the local community, raising money for charitable causes. John Thompson played the accordion, accompanying the singers and fiddlers in the group.

The highlight of the group's show was John's party piece - 'Jake the Peg (deedle, deedle, deedle, dumb!). Rolf Harris would be proud of him. John's passion, though, was his garden. Long before his marriage to Mary, his vegetables were winning prizes at local flower shows. When he was younger, working on shifts, especially six to two, there was plenty free time to spend working on keeping his garden - and, for extra money, he gained a reputation for keeping other people's.

But as his responsibilities at Glen Dufftown grew, time on his other interests diminished, and he found himself walking golf courses for more hours than he cared for. Golf courses on Speyside were becoming a main feature of the landscape, and it seemed that every town was going to have one: Grantown, Dufftown, Keith, Garmouth and Speybay. And let's not forget Rothes: who would ever have thought that Rothes would one day have a golf course?. Such is the power of whisky.

As good as Willie's dad was at growing vegetables, his mum easily equalled him in the Dufftown popularity stakes. Mary Thompson was a master baker, and had crochied her way to stardom many times through her exhibits in the W.R.I. tent at the Keith show.

The 'great' Keith show was one of the Thompson family days out when Willie and his sister Liz were still young enough to go places with their parents.

Other family outings were jaumts to the Tomintoul and Aberlour highland games, and Sunday picnics to the Grouse Inn. Picnics in the hills were usually favoured rather than travel to Lossie, Hopeman or Cullen beaches, for fear of a wasted journey. It may be a hot sunny day in Dufftown, but at the coast the sea har can hang around all day. Sea haar is synonymous only to the East coast.

A big treat on Sunday evenings for the family was having an ice cream from Barclays' van. You could set your watch by Jimmy Barclay's arrival in Dufftown from Keith, the musical chimes from his ice cream van on a still Dufftown evening ringing clear down the length of Conval Street.

At the height of their fame, Barclay's had half a dozen ice cream vans doing regular rounds throughout the area, as well as having a good going restaurant business in Keith.

So good was the trade in ice cream in the North of Scotland that ice cream maker WALLS set up a factory at Jericho in Aberdeenshire. Their ice cream went down particularly well at church fetes and sales of work, where many a man, woman or child would 'Stop Them and Buy One'.

9

Being the only Dufftown born and bred current Highland League footballer, Willie was invited along to open the sale of work at the Memorial hall. Usually it was the Highland Games chieftains job, but this particular year the games chief had gone on holiday to New Zealand to visit his brother who had emigrated there many years previous. Packing his kilt and sporran, as the trip coincided with Highland Games in Sydney, Australia, where the local clan society had arranged duties for him to perform. (What does a Scotsman wear under his kilt down under?)

Close season 1970, thought Willie, would be the right time to take a month off from work, to go to Australia and visit a couple of footballing pals he played with in the Speyside league. Tom Milne and Gordon McDonald had both emigrated as doctors straight from Aberdeen University to Sydney.

Close season at the distillery coincided with the end of the Highland League football season, so it was the ideal time to make the trip. With ten months to save, and plan it all, he put himself forward for extra hours at work. This would be a journey of a lifetime, Willie's first time abroad and his first time flying. Every trip he had embarked on till now was either with his pals, or his parents, so he was determined to do this journey on his own. His itinerary, his decisions, his holiday.

Having done some hitch hiking in Scotland during his teens, he remembered that travelling light was the best plan.

One bag with the bare essentials to be checked in, and a small bag for hand luggage. Willie wandered down to the Fife Arms, ordered a pint, and sat down to plan his trip. Train to Glasgow, stay the night at Ed's, tea time shuttle flight to Heathrow, 10 30pm flight to Singapore, two night stopover, then the midday flight to Perth to stay a week with his cousins, and then the last leg to Sydney, to have a ball with Tom and Gordon.

CHAPTER FOUR

DESTINATION AUSTRALIA

1

The following months flew past with Willie clocking up a few hundred hours of overtime. One more week of six to two and he'd be packing his smalls for the big trip.

On the day of departure, Willie's mum and dad dropped him off at Elgin railway station for his midmorning train to Glasgow. Willie was on his way to Australia!

By the time his pal Ed arrived at Central station Willie was all cappuccinod out, ogling the office girls as they passed to and fro in their city attire. The boys departed, heading for their favourite Chinese restaurant, before having a couple of pints in the Horseshoe bar, and home to Ed's for a whisky night cap. Next day the pals toured some Glasgow sights, and late afternoon Ed dropped Willie off at the airport for his tea time flight to London.

Before doing any window shopping and people watching, Willie decided to check his checking in time and gate number. In no time at all, British Airways flight no. 609 Heathrow to Singapore was called for boarding. An aisle seat would suit Willie fine, handy for when the drinks trolley comes round, and for that other flying pass time, 'which stewardess would you like in your personal space'. British Airways stewardesses are all so beautiful it does take a man with high standards a while to choose. Willie enjoyed a bit of self pampering, so when the pampering is done by such stunning looking woman you do feel a little bit special.

Ping pong! "Good evening ladies and gentlemen, this is your captain Tim Smith speaking. I'd like to welcome you aboard this British Airways flight 609 to Singapore. We'll be cruising at an altitude of 32,000 ft, with a land speed of 565 knots. The weather forecast for our flight is favourable with a moderate tail wind. Head steward Mr McKay, and his cabin crew, are on hand to answer any questions you may have. We'll be landing to refuel at Abu Dhabi before continuing our route to Singapore, and will be on the ground for approximately two hours if you would like to stretch your legs. Thank you for choosing British Airways, and I do hope you have a pleasant flight".

At that point, Willie had a slight pang of fear, as all sorts of things entered his head, like:

"Hope there's no highjackers!"

"Hope there's no lightning storms!"

"Hope there's no bombs!"

"Hope there's no turbulence!"

And, most importantly,

"Hope there's no crash!"

2

Settling down after a pleasant meal, which would knock the socks off most off the Scottish eateries he had been in,

Willie flicked forward and back through the in-flight film choices, wondering how he was ever going to manage to watch them all before the plane lands. Maybe a short sleep would help him make up his mind.

Willie awoke with a start, hoping his snoring had not been too loud for his fellow passengers, and a Singapore airport story came to mind. The central character Peter Sadowski had been en route from New Zealand to Britain and, waiting for his onward flight at Changi, started speaking to a complete stranger to pass the time.

"Where in Scotland are you from Peter?" asked the other guy.

"Oh, I'm from Keith", says Peter.

"The only person I know from Keith is Davie Rough. He's on the rigs."

"I know," says Peter, "It's the same rig I'm on!"

Willie laughed to himself, thinking it was amazing the guy knew where Keith was.

32,000 feet up in a jumbo jet having breakfast with three hundred other passengers beats the Glen Dufftown café any day. Another four hours, and Tim the pilot would be contemplating the plane's descent into Changi airport, so Willie ordered a whisky and settled down to watch a film, adjusting his headphones, and tweaking the volume, to get himself into the film's story.

3

'Ping pong!

"Ladies and gentleman," said the captain over his intercom. "Please return to your seats. Please make sure they are in an upright position, and that your table is locked away. Please fasten your seat belts, as we will be making our descent shortly. Cabin crew, check overhead lockers, and return to your seats. Thank you."

With ears popping, and trying to rub the sweat from the palms of his hands, Willie privately prayed for a safe landing. As the plane bumped the ground, Willie found himself pressing imaginary brake pedal with both feet until the plane slowed to more of a Dufftown pace. A hearty applause filled the cabin - Tim had down his job. In his job there's no room for error. The man did well.

4

Willie's stopover hotel was called the Mandarin, and straight away in the hotel lobby he was addressed by an Asian porter.

"You Scottish gentleman?", said the small man in burgundy high neck tunic.

How had he known? Willie hadn't uttered a word, wasn't wearing his kilt, and he certainly wasn't playing his bagpipes! Immediately he thought, 'It's only an Englishman who can tell a Scotsman at fifty paces! Who is this guy?'

Willie's room was comfortable and, conveniently, on the same floor as the outdoor swimming pool. He beached himself at the edge of the pool, kicked up his feet awhile, thinking, 'If this pool leaks in the middle of the night, there would be a lot of wet dreams down below'.

5

It was time to be out on the streets exploring, as there was a lot to pack into two days. First he needed to change some of his Scottish pounds, and the canny Scot in him said he'd get a better price on the street. Literally ten paces from the hotel front door two guys with a folding card table and a fistful of dollars were offering a bit more for his Scottish twenty than the hotel Bureau De Change.

Willie set off, chuffed with his street plan to absorb the city atmosphere and see the sights. As darkness fell, Willie found himself wandering through a shopping arcade, similar to Inverness's Victorian market.

Suddenly, from out of nowhere, a man appeared. Although Willie couldn't see anywhere that resembled a gents outfitter - or any clothes shop for that matter - Willie had a measuring tape across his shoulders before he could blink.

"Italian suit sir, only one hundred dollar!"

"No thanks," said Willie forcefully, quickening his pace and wondering how an Asian making a suit in Asia using material probably made in Asia constitutes an *Italian* suit! But on looking back, the wee guy was up on him again.

"You want suit? Special price for you - seventy five dollar."

By now, Willie was aware that the arcade lighting wasn't bright and that if he refused this man's suit offer would he call up his 'Triad' pals. Willie sprinted the next hundred yards in ten seconds.

6

Back at the hotel bar, Willie downed a large whisky.

"We'll put it on your room account sir," said the waitress, and as he savoured the last bead of nectar another double was on his table. 'This could go on all evening', thought Willie, 'unless I get up and leave'. He got up and left!

But the whisky had aroused his appetite. He was hungry now, ravenous, and wanted the best Chinese meal ever. Within a three minute walk he had a choice of restaurants to gorge himself in.

Some dim sums, tiger beer, chicken curry, spare ribs, fried rice to die for, and lychees to finish. He ate his fill, and enjoyed every morsel, except for the chicken foot placed on top of the curry dish. Was Willie supposed to take it home, dry it out, and hang it round his neck, or was it just the year of the chicken?

Willie wandered around a few streets before returning to his hotel bar for a nightcap, and to his surprise this time there was an Asian female guitar slinger, singing Bob Dylan songs. Two large whiskies and he was nearly in heaven.

7

Willie's second day in Singapore took on more of a cultural feel to it. Changi prison museum, Buddhist temples housing giant ornamental Buddha's, botanical gardens, and the famous Raffles Hotel.

By tea time he was all Singapored out, and needed to get back to his hotel pool before collapsing with the humidity. This time he was sharing the pool with Mary and George from Belfast, Northern Ireland. George was in the Guarda police, and hoping to reach his twenty two years service without being blown up. The couple was en-route to Sydney to visit their son and his family who had emigrated there ten years previously. This was their second trip to Australia, and had strong feelings about retiring there to become Sydney siders.

Next morning, Willie phoned the airline to confirm his onward journey before breakfast. Singapore hotel breakfasts for Willie was a bit special. He liked the idea of helping himself to what he fancied before setting out on his onward journey. It was the first time he had seen a rotary toaster, so he had two extra slices just to watch it working.

As fully fuelled as the Quantas jumbo, Willie was excited and eager to be airborne again on the flight path to Perth. For Mary and George it would be another twelve hours before they touched down in sunny Sydney, but for Willie, Perth and his relatives were waiting. His Uncle Richard, auntie Pamela, and cousins, Billy and Isabel would bestow him a warm welcome.

Approaching Perth international airport, Willie was thinking, 'It's nae very big this Perth, but it has to be bigger than Perth, Scotland, surely'.

Ping pong!

"Thank you for flying with Quantas. On behalf of Captain Bruce McKenzie, my crew, and myself, we hope you had a pleasant flight. G-day."

Going through immigration, Willie couldn't get over the passport man in his shorts and short sleeved shirt. It was midnight, a time when Scots people are pullin' on an extra jersey, but as the airport doors parted in front of Willie he was engulfed with a waft of warm, balmy air.

"Weel, weel", said Richard in his broad Banffshire accent. "Had a good flight? I see you like to travel wi' the best o' airlines - nice an' generous wi' the Johnny Walker!"

"'How far's the hoose, Richard? I need a Johnny

Walker and I need it right noo!" said an over-excited Willie.

"Do you nae see enough whisky, working' wi' it? We're beer an' red wine drinkers, Willie, but we can stop off at the bottle drivethrough."

"No, no, I love red wine Richard. It's becoming my favourite drink. I had some Australian Merlot on the plane and it was just delicious, so fruity."

Thirty minutes later and they were at Richard's home in Gosnells, a sprawling suburb of Perth where the rest of Richards clan were waiting to give Willie a big Aussie welcome. Shared stories and fortified wine helped Willie to wind down from the excitement of being in Australia.

8

Next morning, the bright continuous sunshine woke Willie about seven am. And as he lay awhile in semi consciousness he could hear the sound of a hoover sweeping its way forward and back over a floor.

'That's not the normal noise a hoover makes at home,' he thought. As he walked bare foot to the living room, he realised why - all the floors were laminated.

"Mornin' Willie," said Richard, bare chested, with bare feet, dressed only in a pair of shorts with the living room window blinds closed. Was this to save the neighnours' embarrassment?

"Do you not open your blinds in the morning Richard?" Willie asked, as at home it was the first thing everybody does.

"No, Willie, we keep them closed till late afternoon when the sun goes round a bit - it helps to protect the furniture from fading and us from cooking!"

It was only eight am, but already the temperature was heading up the late teens. Richard was sure today's temperature would easily match yesterday's high of thirty-two. His advice to Willie was stay indoors between ten and two, and at all other times not to stray far from the pool.

More wise advice came from Pamela as she offered breakfast. "Don't go out without a wide brimmed hat - take your pick from the collection at the door." The last time Willie had seen so many hats was at his cousin's wedding in Dufftown two years previously.

Willie chose the hat that looked most like a Stetson - he'd always wanted to be a cowboy, and had already thought of planning a holiday in Canada's Rocky Mountains.

After breakfast, Willie took a walk in the 'back yard', stepping out onto the garden path slabs in his bare feet.

"Wow, these are hot! Oucha, oucha, oucha... These blighters are hot."

"Don't go out without your thongs on!" shouted Richard.

'Thongs?' thought Willie.'That's a bit near the bone for a Dufftown lad.'

"Did you say *songs* or *thongs* Richard?" asked a confused Willie.

"Thongs, Willie, for your feet!"

"Oh, you mean flip flops!" said Willie, relieved.

"Yeah, you never go out without your thongs, sunnies, and hat."

Willie took a short walk over the sunburnt back lawn, through a sandy area of ground where lush green vegetation seemed to separate the properties. On a nearby gum tree, a pair of Parakeets were conversing, and next door a cluster of Cockatoos were sunning themselves, discussing whose garden to fly to next. Willie had arrived, he was as near paradise as he could have wished. People should be cautious of their first impressions, but two weeks, and hundreds of Western Australian miles later, he was of the same opinion.

Richard had a catch phrase, which amused Willie. While lying back on a lylow with something substantial from the barbecue in one hand and a well-charged glass of red wine in the other, Richard would say, "I wonder what the poor people are doing now?"

Willie's thoughts were always of his family at home, each time Richards saying was aired. His family were living in the Greyness of Dufftown, while Willie basked under a blue sky that went on forever. Willie had found his perfect Shangri-La, and still had the delights of Sydney to come.

9

In two days, it would be up and up into that endless blue skies, flying East across Australia for five hours to New South Wales and Sydney.

For the first time, Willie was realising how large Australia was. He checked a map of the world in the in-flight magazine to compare Oz to Scotland. Willie hadn't been that brilliant with geography at school, but thought he had a reasonable grasp of the globe's picture in his mind. To his amazement, the staple holding the magazine pages together was covering the whole of Scotland.

'To cover Australia with staples', thought Willie, 'you would need at least ten boxes'.

The cabin steward greeted him jovially. "G-day sir,"

he said, "What can I get you?"

"I'll have a large whisky and ice please," answered Willie, secretly hoping the steward wouldn't present him with some Aussie equivalent of Scotch.

"There you go, mate," said the steward as he handed Willie a Johnny Walker red label miniature.

"I'm gonna enjoy this flight," mused Willie, "This airline serves its customers some good stuff!"

By 1970, Johnny Walker was a long established brand, but some of Speyside's best drams had yet to be made. Whisky has this old reputation: 'the older the spirit, the better the dram'/ But that's a myth of the ad men. Distillery workers know better, though they wouldn't dare tell you.

Along with his Johnny Walker miniature, Willie was handed the dinner menu. 'Classy touch,' thought Willie. 'These Aussies'll go far, yet we don't see that many at the visitors' centre. Mainly it's Japanese, Italians, Germans, and Americans, Ah, well, it's early days yet. Better have another whisky before dinner.'

He remembered his granddad always use to say, 'Two afore denner is better than three efter'.

From the menu he chose the Chicken Chasseur, with green whole beans, and pommes frites. Asking for two bottles of red wine, he didn't consider himself greedy - after all, the bottles were tiny. With coffee and mints to finish a great meal, it was time to watch a film. What puzzled Willie was the incredible organization behind the meal times. Three hundred odd people to feed, with a choice of two hot main dishes, and then with little fuss, the trays are all cleared, and stacked into a trolley that measures fourteen inches wide by thirty six inches long, (a feat Paul Daniels would be proud of). Within two hours from take off, you've been watered, feed, and ready to relax, and enjoy the in-flight movie. Willie was impressed.

10

Willie's excitement was building, as he was only two hours away from touch down in Sydney. Tom and Gordon would be there to greet him, and the party could begin. Mates in Sydney, half a world away from home, surely they couldn't get up to any mischief. If Perth appealed to Willie as the relaxant city of Australia, Sydney was sure to be the party town.

The midday flight flew steadily on, and nobody could have prepared Willie for the magnificent views he captured as his plane banked round over the city for landing inwards from the sea. Breathtaking.

Coming through immigration was a trial for Willie, because the overcautious Australian authorities demanded that all passengers remove their footwear and place them on the x-ray belt with the hand luggage. Before belting up in preparation for landing, the cabin crew went mad wi' spray cans (was it just Willie, or did all the Scots get a double dose?).

Once again the passport man was in shorts and short sleeved shirt (no tongue twister meant) but he seemed cooler than Perth;s passport man. And even more laid back.

Eventually through the checkout, Willie had a big smile on his face, smiling back at the dozens of cheery Asian faces with their name boards. Willie was feeling the Aussie wave of laid-back-ness wash over him.

'I like this country,' he was thinking to himself, when

from the sea of happy Asians two recognisable semi-suntanned Scotsman appeared and hugged Willie, like he'd just scored the winner for the Villa.

"Do we take the tube into town?" Willie asked,

"No," says Tom, "We're in town. Everywhere in Sydney is in Sydney, just the same as Dufftown."

"Fancy a Chinese, guys? Or do you want to get a shower first, Willie, and a change of thongs?" asked Gordon.

"Nice one, Gordon, but you're forgetting I stopped over in Perth at my auntie and uncle's for two weeks, I know what thongs are in Australia!" boasted Willie. He was seasoning himself with the Aussie lingo, and he gave a demonstration:

"I'll bet the Sheilas are pretty nice, Bruce, in their sunnies and thongs."

"Is that a mechanical, digger?"

"Strewth, mate, he's a snappy little fella..."

Willie was lapping it up, Sydney was his kind of scene. Australia wasn't so much a country where the grass was greener, but a place where the sky was always bluer.

11

Gordon and Tom shared a town house in North Sydney, a five minute ferry ride across Sydney harbour from Circular Quay. From their second story balcony, they had fantastic views of daily harbour life, and the downtown Sydney skyline.

"Wait till you see that view lit up at night, Willie," says Gordon. "After two weeks o' this wonderful city, you'll never want to leave."

Showered, shaved, and after a welcoming ice-cold

beer from the beer fridge, the trio hopped onto the shuttle ferry, following their noses and bellies to Chinatown.

On their approach to Chinatown, strains of English ballad-type songs filtered through the clammy evening air, and as they neared the heart of restaurant land they caught a glimpse of the culprit - a pony-tailed Asian guy in his thirties serenading the diners in perfect English. Tom Jones fans were in their element, eating the best food in the world and listening to their favourite songs (the boys chose a table not too close).

After their feed, they wandered back to Circular Quay, which was thronging with overdressed poseurs in full flight, displaying their finery to the passing world.

"What's going on?" asked Willie.

"It's Sydney sider time," answers Tom.

"What?" says Willie, "They all drink cider."

"Ha ha, Willie, they're out in force at this time, the siders, they dress to impress, have a couple of drinks in the plush bars, then go out on booze cruises for two hours, get pished, and scuff their good shoes staggering hame. They're great fun to watch."

"Tomorrow we'll have lunch at Darling harbour. Prawns an' beer for five dollars, and they have the biggest selection of smoothes in Sydney. We could take a look round the maritime museum, there's a battleship, an' sub, then we'll go on to the national history museum."

Tom and Gordon were eager to impress, and give Willie a memorable holiday.

Gordon suggested: "What about sittin' down tonight wi' a couple of beers and plan what you want to do, Willie, and where we can go in the next two weeks?"

"Bondi beach babes top the list," laughed Willie.

"Then on my last day we'll do the Blue Mountains."

"No worries, Willie, except the only difference between Bondi beach, and Lossie beach, is that Bondi gets more sun.

12

So that evening, sitting out on the North Sydney balcony, their two week itinerary was constructed. Deciding on a seven day motor home hire, they would go wine hunting in the Hunter valley by travelling up through Central coast, returning to Sydney via the Blue Mountains, giving Willie another few days and nights to do all the touristy things. Then the Opera house, Botanical gardens, A M P Tower, climbing the coat hanger - and some more Chinatown meals, of course. Stuff that any tourist visiting Sydney, should not leave the city without doing.

All agreed, they cracked open a Merlot from the Hunter valley, threw some steaks on the barbie, and as Willie sat back to take in the Sydney skyline he couldn't help but think of his uncle Richard's saying, "What are the poor people doing now?"

Life at that very moment for Willie could not get any better

Dusk was falling over the Opera house, and every few seconds the floodlighting was making the concert hall more dramatic. The skyline high-rise buildings were quickly changing from a mass of reflected sunlight to millions of small lights all in regimental pose.

"This must be one of the best nighttime skyscapes in the world," enthused Willie. "You guys have got it sussed, living in a fabulous city with a fantastic climate, where nobody gets the cold, which means less hours in your surgeries, and more time looking at this view. I want to emigrate here, and start my own distillery! You guys would be manager and brewer. I'd call it, 'Glen Sydney', a malt whisky made in Australia with sunshine in every dram."

It was a great dream - but only for three and a half nanoseconds when till Tom and Gordon reminded Willie that Australians only drink beer and wine!

13

Next morning the three Scotsman were up with the early sun, checking out the motor home rental companies in the city. Soon they found one to suit their needs, and the next stop was a supermarket to stock up. By lunch time they had the freedom of the Pacific Coast Highway, heading for Central Coast.

Checking the New South Wales visitors guide as they motored North, the first port of call would be the Australian Reptile Park at Somersbay, less than an hour from the city. This was the home of 'Eric', the most famous crocodile in New south Wales. During one of Eric's many fight encounters in the wild, he had lost one of his forelegs but gained celebrity status.

"Next stop after will be the Entrance," said Gordon. "They feed the pelicans there. I've heard that hundreds gather at the same time every day. The only trouble is, I don't know when feeding time is. Well, if we miss the feeding time tomorrow, we'll just stay over. the Entrance, I believe, is a lively spot."

Tom was at the wheel while Gordon had the job of navigator. The doctors were just a few months into their second year in Australia, but until now had not been north of the city boundary. This was as much of an adventure for them as it was for Willie.

Staying on the coast road, passing Norah Head lighthouse, they headed inland through Wyee, rejoining the Pacific highway in pursuit of the Hunter Valley wineries. All they knew of the Hunter Valley was what they read in their tourist guide, and of the one hundred and fourteen wineries mentioned only Lindemans rang a bell.

The day's temperature was peaking at twenty five degrees, and Willie, feeling the heat in the camper, kept wanting to open the windows.

"No, No Willie, keep the windows shut an' we'll get the air conditioning on - once we've sussed out how to operate it!"

"Good job it's nae summer time, Willie. When we came to Oz, January last year, for the first week or two the heat was unbearable! I thought, wi' you havin' two weeks in Perth you would be climatised''.

"It doesnae take much heat to make a Scotsman's blood boil," snapped Willie, feelin' a wee bit neitry.

"Just relax, Willie! It's the Aussie way," laughed Tom, "We'll stop for a dip in the next river we come to, guaranteed no crocs, snakes, or spiders."

Gordon said: "What did the guy at the Reptile Park say? As long as you get to a doctor within two days of the bite, you'll live... or was it two hours of the bite? But anyway, spiders don't like Scots people, they're too thick skinned!"

Leaving the highway, Tom pulled the camper over at a rocky area beside the river. Cautious from past horror stories from the Australian bush, Willie reluctantly paddled his feet, splashing himself over with water, checking every few seconds for fear of being ambushed by the dreaded red back or funnel web spiders. Scared o' the great Australian bight, Willie.

14

Within an hour of being back on the wine trail, the motor home was cruising through the lush rolling landscape of the Hunter Valley. Row upon row of vines, as far as the eye could see, with beautiful, tastily constructed reception centres, glinting in the sun, on either side of the long winding road down the valley. Following the signs to the central shopping area, the guys were keen to park up, and sample the wine.

Thinking the wineries would be similar to distillery tours, they entered the nearest reception area, and were delighted to find they didn't have to go through the laborious business of listening to a tour guide before getting to taste what they came for.

Six wineries later, the guys were tryin' to convince each other that visiting the other one hundred and eight wouldn't take that long if they only had one glass in each. What they did agree on, was staying three nights parked in the valley, one night on the back road to the Blue Mountains, and two nights in the Blue Mountains.

Slowly, one by one, they dropped off to sleep, listening to the crickets, and dreaming of the next days tasting. Willie wasn't a great riser in the morning - getting up for the six am to two pm shift at the distillery was always a struggle, especially in mid winter. When he was with the warehouse staff some days the only time he saw daylight, was walking from warehouse to warehouse. But with the Australian sun, and the chirping cockatoos, he found he was waking up between five and six am, and eager to get up to explore the day ahead.

Over breakfast in the restaurant, the guys planned their route round the tasting rooms, throughout the valley. For a very reasonable fare 'Prince' the Clydesdale horse, with his decorative coach, was available to carry visitors around the wineries.

"So what do you think of Australia, Willie?" asked Tom.

"It's big and it's hot Tom!" replied Willie.

"I wasn't asking about the size of your willie, Willie, what about Australia?"

By mid morning, they were at their third winery of the day, another two, and they'd be stopping at Lindemans for lunch. In the court yard of Lindemans, stood a well appointed barbecue for the visitors' use. At the butcher counter, you would select the steak of your choice, heap onto your plate as much salad as you wished, and with a glass of red or white wine, the total bill was only six dollars. You, of course, had to barbecue your own steak. Coming from Dufftown, that was learning a completely new skill for Willie. Most folk in Dufftown wouldn't know what a barbecue was, far less have tasted any food prepared on one. If a Dufftown house had a barbecue area in its back garden it could only mean that the previous occupier was from down south, and after their first summer and winter in Dufftown, probably moved to the lower lying Laich o' Moray.

One of Willie's first observations which puzzled him on his Australian holiday, was how do clothes shops survive? Surely they get government aid, cos if there's one thing you don't need in Australia it's clothes. A change of t-shirt and shorts, twice a day in the hot weather, a jumper and light trousers for winter evenings, and maybe socks, that's it. Not like in Dufftown, where it's the exact opposite, two pairs of everything on at the same time - all year round.

By late afternoon, the Poplar trees on the sloops of the valley were casting a lengthening shadow, not that the wine soaked heroes had noticed, they were in wine heaven, buying up some favourite vintages to savour back in Sydney.

"Just one more winery," roared Gordon. "Red wine's really good for you, especially by the bottle - trust me, I'm a doctor!"

They were now the last passengers on Prince's carriage for the day, and were probably the drunkest three Scotsman he had ever taxied home.

15

An early breakfast next morning, and they were on the road South, heading for the Blue Mountains. Had they stayed another day in the Hunter Valley, the wine drinking may have lead to further embarrassment for the Scotsman abroad.

Katoomba, the largest town in the Blue Mountain area, was a good five or six hours drive.

This time Tom took the wheel, saying, "We'll stop for lunch in about three hours."

Willie was thinking: 'Christ, three hours without a break, is it a race or something?;

"Could we nae stop every hour for a break, an' check out the scenery? Willie asked. "I'm nae used to these long drives. I've got to stop for a rest driving fae Dufftown to Elgin!"

An hour down the road, Tom pulls over. "Does anybody fancy a short bush walk?" Tom enquired of his passengers. But on switching off the engine and turning round, he found them both asleep. Not wanting to disturb the peace, Tom adjusted his seat back, and also drifted off for a snooze. The previous two days wine tastings were taking their toll on the winery mutineers, tiredness was hampering their getaway to the splendour and majesty of the Blue Mountains.

16

After an hour-long cat nap, their batteries were recharged, and they yawned their way back onto the road from the dusty layby.

"I've heard the Blue Mountains are where the Sydney folk go ski-ing," said Gordon.

"Aye, but it canna be real snow, they must hae wheels on their skis, you dinna get snow in Australia," insisted Willie.

"Well, we've never seen Aussie snow, but apparently it does exist," disagreed Gordon.

"I didn't come all the way to Australia to see snow! At the first sight o' the bloody stuff we head home to Sydney!"

Willie was getting a bit paranoid. Having been brought up in the Cabrach, and Dufftown, Willie had seen more than his fair share of it. Cabrach winters started in October, going through until March - and some years even in April, snow showers would make the Cabrach to Dufftown road treacherous. It had been known that in some years the harvest would be as late as December, and instead of taking in the new year Cabrach farmers were taking in the harvest - bringing in the bales instead of ringing in the bells!!!

There were only three seasons in the Cabrach year: winter, rainy season, and summer. Summer was a mixture of Spring and Autumn with a sprinkling of sunny days, (warm enough to take your jacket off). The long evenings of June, July and August were Willie's favourite times. Sitting out for hours in the field above the croft, usually with his border collie, Patch, listening to the lapwings, and skylarks across the fields. Through the still summer evening air, would drift the sound of neighbouring crofters, as they checked on their sheep and cattle. '*Come by, come by.*'

The Cabrach is a high lying area of scattered hill farms, with poor soil conditions, making it more suited to grazing sheep than growing arable crops, but the rolling hilly landscape rests easy on the eyes, and the territory has an atmosphere of calming to it. Willie had just turned ten when the Thompson clan moved from the family croft to live in Dufftown. It just seemed more practical to be in the town, as both parents were working at the distillery.

Another good reason for flitting was the condition of the croft house, which lacked a few mod cons of the post-war era, and was badly in need of a complete renovation. Parts of the Cabrach are like that rarest of places, which draw you, and make you feel a sense of longing. The Thompson croft was a holding of thirty or so acres tucked in behind a hillock out of eye shot from the road, and had been farmed by the Thompson clan down through the generations. Willie's generation would be the first not to raise family there, among the collection of hens, ducks, and geese. If Willie was going to have children one day, they would grow up as toonies in Dufftown. The old ways of Scottish country life in the Cabrach for them would be nothing more than a Sunday drive from Dufftown to Rhynie, with Willie saying, "Now that's where your granny and granddad used to live," fondly recalling his cherished memories of growing up on the croft.

For as long as anyone can remember, the social centre of the Cabrach has been the aptly named The Pheasants Rest where mums and dads from neighbouring farms would socialise at the weekends. It wasn't uncommon to see a couple of tractors and Land Rovers in the car park during weekdays, as hill farming can be thirsty work. Two things the Pheasants Rest was famed for was its fabulous collection of whisky miniatures, and the wall clock that went backwards.

(Maybe the clock should be explained! Instead of the numbers on the face going clockwise, they went anticlockwise. Greenwich time wasn't Cabrach time, Cabrach time was Cabrach time. One of the few places where time can stand still - if you give it time to!)

Further on is the heather moor land of the Upper Cabrach, inhabited by grouse and pheasant, surrounding the 'Buck o' the Cabrach'. The road then descends steadily to Rhynie (but that's getting dangerously close to Aberdeenshire).

Changing schools for Willie was a wee bit daunting. They may only have been nine miles apart, but moving from the coothieness of Cabrach primary to the more street-wise Mortlach school, Willie found he wasn't quite as sharp as the toonies were, in the playground. There were new after school games he hadn't heard of, but being keen on furthering his education he made pals with the street teachers almost right away. Plundering, spoot rumbling, door bell ringing, checking phone boxes for loose change, were just some of the mischievous games they would get up to. The streets of Dufftown were a whole new playground for Willie, and he soon forgot his anxieties about moving from the Cabrach.

17

The Blue Mountains were within sight, and Willie looked long and hard to see if there were any snow-capped peaks, but thankfully it was an exceptionally warm winter so peace prevailed in the camper.

Parking up in Katoomba for a meal stop, the guys were taken aback by the Wild West-ness of the town. It had definitely been designed and built by an Arizona based building firm. The only thing missing were saddled horses tied up outside the saloon doors. The charm of the town was endless. Menu A boards littered the canopy covered pavements. Outdoor eateries at every street corner offered barbecue steak in as many sizes as people have appetites.

Not really knowing which restaurant to opt for, they did paper, rock, scissors, until it came down to Willie's choice. He was in an exotic mood, and chose the restaurant that offered on its A board Kangaroo and crocodile steaks, Wallaby wings, snake steaks, Lizard lungs, and other off the wall Aussie bush tucker.

A scrumptious feed, and the bush men were ready to take on whatever the Blue Mountains had to offer.

"What's first guys? Will it be the chair lift, or the funicular railway?" asked Tom. "Lets get an information leaflet, we don't want to miss anything."

After digesting the booklet 'What to do in the Blue Mountains over a glass of beer', it was decided that if they were going to explore the area thoroughly, it would be best to park up and stay over, otherwise they were rushing their visit.

The tourist office and shop, overlooking the three sisters' view, reeled in the visitors who were keen on declaring to the world they'd got their latest t-shirt in Australia's Blue Mountains.

18

Next morning the guys pulled on their hiking boots for a five-mile rain forest walk. Down to the forest floor via the almost vertical funicular railway, past the authentic slate mine adorned with relics left decaying under the coolness of the forest canopy. Every few metres, shafts of sunlight pierced the pathway as they followed the marker signs deeper into the valley. As long as they didn't stray too far from the marker posts they wouldn't get lost.

Walking in a sub tropical rain forest was a complete surprise for Willie. When the subject of Australia came up at home the very last thought talking about Australia would conjure up was rain. Australia was all sun, bush, and beer. Men called Bruce with wine bottle corks dangling from their hats, and women called Sheilas, all blonde an' brown, and wrinkly. It's the foreigners' perception, of course, like Scotsmen all wear kilts and play the bagpipes - except in Willie's case that was true.

Tired and hungry after their forest trek, they feasted themselves in the three sisters' restaurant, with a cold beer or two to follow. The day was slipping away, and with the cable car ride still to do it could mean staying in the heart of the 'Blues' another night.

"Yeah, guys, let's just have another couple of beers, and leave the cable car experience for tomorrow," said the exhausted Willie. "We should relax here an' watch the sun goin' down over the three sisters. That'll do us today."

"No worries, Willie, we might even meet some Shelias to talk to an' have a beer with."

No sooner were the words out of Tom's mouth than three pairs of eyes scanned the busy restaurant, and lo an' behold not too far from their table sat three Aussie girls, who, like themselves, were visiting the Blue Mountains from Sydney. But the boys weren't too hasty, the night was young, and they'd lots to chat about amongst themselves.

"So how's the job goin' at Glen Duffers Willie? Are you still enjoying it?"

"That's ten years now, guys, I'm part of the fixtures an' fittings. When I first went onto shifts, though, six to two was hard - I hae tae get up at five. I have suggested they revolve the shift clock round a bit, like making the first shift eight to four, then four to twelve, and twelve to eight. Now that's much more civilized. Just think, if that was to happen, it would revolutionise distillery workers' lives for ever."

Tom and Gordon agreed.

"So whisky's nae a big seller in Australia? We'll need to change that," said Willie. "Speyside's liquid gold should be slidin' doon Aussie throats like the Spiy in spate."

"What's your plans wi' the career then Willie?" asked Gordon.

"Well hopefully, work my way up to still manager if I can. Play fitba' for another three or four seasons, build a hoose somewhere between Dufftown, Aberlour an' the Craig, or up the Cabrach, and live a happy contented life, retiring at sixty to play golf. How's that?"

"Sounds like it's a better life than a doctor's - and we've had to train for six, seven years, living in student squalor, penniless, on beans on toast."

"You guys sound homesick! You've only jist got here and you're already pinin' for the splendour of Speyside. The greyness, the drizzle, the razor sharp north wind, wearin' socks. Boys, boys, come to your senses! Living in Australia is the best life anyone can have - especially Scottish doctors."

"Wise words, Willie Whisky. You're a mature twenty five-year-old pure Speyside malt!" They all laughed at Tom's quip.

"I like that! Yeah, you can call me Willie Whisky. It kinda fits, Is that Willie wi' a y ? 'Willy Whisky'. I've come all the way to Australia to be christened, baptised in Aussie wine - nae the distillery low wines but the full bodied Australian Merlot. What an honour. Better have a dram to keep it Scottish, though. You know the secret o' drinkin' whisky, guys?" asked Willie. Seeing blank faces, he explained, "Never miss your mouth!"

They all laughed again.

"Being Scottish doctors in Oz! Is that nae just the best job in the world?" asked Willie, paused for the kill. They bronzed Sheilas, man, wi' the skin cancer scare thing, you could have your hands all over them. Speak aboot putty in your hands. I can only think of only one drawback in bein' a Scottish doctor in Australia - spider bites! You guys can handle midgy bites, and the odd gleg bite, but what do you do when the redback strikes? Uh!"

Willie hadn't neglected the three likely looking Shielas. He had kept his beady eyes on them all the while, and now that the girls' glasses were getting nearer empty than they were full, he realised that the time was ripe for the guys to make a move.

First to the girls table, was the debonair Gordon (the Robert Redford of the group), close on his heels followed Tom,

"How ya goin' girls, can we buy you a beer?"

"Can you tell what we are yet?" said Willie, after which he made noises supposed to resemble Rolf Harris's wobble board.

"Well," said one of the girls, "he's not Australian!" She indicated Willie who, by this time, was beaming from head to toe at his favourite of the three girls.

"It's my round," Willie insisted, "Beers all round is it? Six for sex barman please - I mean six four x please, mate."

The barman half cracked a smile, thinking, 'Oh, well it looks like it could be an entertaining evening'.

Willie didn't really like cold beer, and was glad it was the Australian wintertime, so this beer was a few degrees above freezing. In summer, he'd been told, bar staff keep the beer, and the GLASSES in the deep freeze.

The more the beer, the looser the tongues, and the looser the tongues, the more the laughs. The evening shot past, and the six friends found themselves pairing off, and strolling in three different directions through the tepid evening air, with only the sound of the crickets for company.

19

Dawn in the Blue Mountains, and waking up with a beautiful, blonde, sun tanned Australian girlfriend, made Willie think he'd died and gone to heaven, but the ever practical Willie didn't let his heart rule his head - after all, he had a career in whisky to think of! And as the girls were on a route North, the group made their farewells after a communal breakfast, when Sydney phone numbers were exchanged.

Striking a course for Sydney, the guys felt good when back in town they had contact numbers to ring, keeping them ahead in the social scene.

"Well," says Tom, "We've done about a thousand miles now and never seen a kangaroo, I had *hopped* for a sighting!"

"Yeah, you're funny Tom, but don't give up the day job," advised Willie, "Jokes like that won't even make your patients' funny bone laugh."

"I've got a joke," pipes Willie, "Did you hear about the guy who didn't know the difference between incense and arson? He set fire to his sister!"

"Boom boom!" said Tom. "But *insest* would have worked better!"

"I've got one," spouts Gordon,

And so it went, blah, blah, blah...

"When we get back to Sydney, we'll have to do the cultural tour, guys," said Willie

"Huh, that won't take long, Willie. Whatever you want to know about Aussie culture, I'll tell you over a smoothie at Darling harbour - trust me I'm a doctor!"

And he did: "There's not much to know. Captain

Cook landed at Botany Bay two hundred years ago, then ten years after that, they shipped all Britain's convicts here, they bred sheep, until the gold rush came along, and brought the Chinese. It's a hard job noo finding a Scottish voice among all the foreigners, just like Grange, aside Keith, or the glen o' Newmill. But have you noticed, all the Australians have the same accent? The East coasters just sound the same as the Perth people, go ten miles in Moray or Banffshire, and you hear a different accent, go to the Broch and Peterheed, and you can't understand anybody. They claim it's English, but it's as legible as Japanese!"

20

Back in Sydney with the motor home safely returned, and their deposit intact, they headed to the nearest bar to quench the thirst they'd been FOSTERing for the past four or five hours.

"Godstrewth, guys, that's good nectar! Drop of the best that is."

"It's only cos you're really thirsty, Willie, Tartan Special would taste good when you're as thirsty as this."

"Yeah but there's definitely something sweeter about this Aussie lager, at home remember, if the lager was a bit bitter, we'd put lime in it. Even with this stuff bein' as cold as this, it still tastes sweeter."

"I can tell you'd like to be an Aussie, Willie, everything here seems to be to your liking. So what's it gonna be - Scottish stills or Aussie thrills?"

"I'd dearly love to live in Sydney, guys, but my distillery career is well on track, I'll be on for a still man when I go back, then a spell in the office, and by the time

I'm thirty or so, I could be on for brewer. Sandy McDonald retires in aboot six or seven years time, just after my dad, and I may even end up one o' the youngest managers on Speyside. I'll be on the big money then, I'd be able to afford to do Australia twice a year, close season and Christmas!"

"Well, we'll still be here, maybe married with kids, in another city perhaps, but definitely still in Australia. It's such a huge country to explore. Here we are, mid twenties, we've seen all of Scotland, but it'll take us the rest of our lives to see all round Australia." said Gordon.

"Yeah, it's fuckin' huge, isn't it?" agreed Tom.

"Okay guys, let's plan tomorrow," said Gordon. "What about the coat hanger climb in the morning, then lunch at Darling harbour, and a boat tour from Circular quay?"

"Sounds like a good day, lets go for it," said Willie.

"Well that leaves two days, Willie," said Tom.

"We'll need a day at Bondi beach - I canna go back to Dufftown without a day on the beach! And I've got to go on a booze cruise."

Tom said, "Willie, no worries. The big silver bird will take you away from Australia a happy and satisfied man."

"Yeah but two hours into the flight and I'll be needing to come back."

"Don't mention leaving, it's three days yet, and it'll be three days that'll pass in the blink of an eye."

"Two blinks more, and I'll be back in the mash room in dungarees, woolly socks, an' boots, wonderin' why I'm depressed and unsettled."

"You've got the hots for Oz, Willie. We'll see you back here before too long."

"Fuck sake, I'm nae away yet! Anyway, you guys will

be home to Aberlour for a holiday before I get back here! But whose round is it? asked a grumpy Willie.

The end of his holiday was within sight, and although Tom and Gordon had been great hosts, Willie was feeling envious of their Sydney lifestyle, and he didn't relish the thought of the airport farewells. A gentle smile however, crossed his face as his next beer arrived in front of him. Another two beers, and the alcohol would ease the pain of leaving behind his New South Wales odyssey, and a carry-out of Chinatown dim sums saw the trio safely onto the late evening ferry to North Sydney.

Next morning they drove over the coat hanger. Since arriving in Sydney, Willie was puzzled by the bridge's nickname 'coathanger', because nobody in Australia would know what a coat was. He insisted it should be renamed 't-shirt hanger'. The last lunch beckoned in Chinatown, and Willie soaked up the oriental atmosphere for the final time on the trip.

With one last look at the blue, blue Sydney skies, Willie trundled through the opening automatic doors to the check-in desk. Tom and Gordon were on hand to offer the reluctant traveler their fond farewells. All checked in, it was time for a last coffee before Willie's late afternoon departure. The conversation was light hearted with a couple of flying jokes thrown in for good measure. Misty eyed, Willie joined the other two hundred-odd passengers in the departure lounge, trying to get his head round the fact that this was the trip home. Unlike the journey East he was flying from Sydney blueness in the Southern hemisphere to the Grey driechness of Dufftown. If the sun was out when he got home, it would be a miracle.

"Two blinks," he remembered saying to Tom and

Gordon, ”and I’ll be pullin’ on my regulation dungarees“. How right he was, after the first week back at work flashed past, it was like he’d never been away. His holiday now seemed like another time, another world, and another life.

CHAPTER FIVE

BACK ON THE WHISKY TRAIN

1

Close season was over, and Glen Dufftown's staff was in full flow with production.

"How was your holiday, Willie? Did you get your hands on any Aussie Sheilas?"

"No, I only had a cuddle fae a Koala!"

The distillery banter on Australia took Willie straight back to the bush, rekindling dozens of memories. It was maybe driech in Dufftown, but the pictures in his head were of brilliant sunshine.

A month into the new distilling season, a staff reshuffle saw Willie being offered a still man's post. The long and winding road to manager status was beginning to straighten out in front of him. Keep his nose clean, and he could be there in ten years, or even less.

Pre season training was about to start at Borough Briggs, and after his holiday excesses, Willie found it tough going. For the first time in six or seven seasons, getting match fit was taking him that bit longer than his teammates. He was now also having to consider his work commitments, with the shift patterns ruling him out of training and playing only one week in three. Maybe the time was right to lay aside his football boots in favour of picking up his golf clubs. Having weighed up the pros and cons of his life at that time, he declined Elgin City's signing on offer, retiring himself from Highland League football at the age of twenty-six. So the feet that scored some of the best and most memorable goals of the past eight seasons would now be treading golf courses instead of gracing football grounds.

2

It was August, and summertime had come to Dufftown. The town was sparkling, crystals in the Skye marble of the harled houses caught the sun and glinted as far down the street as you could see. Speyside colours were at their summer best, bright yellow whins and broom clung to the Cabrach hillside, as Willie took a run in his new mini cooper (even the name of his car related to whisky).

The evenings were warm and long; this was Willie's favourite time. He'd loved the brightness and heat of the Australian sun, but long warm Scottish evenings were special. When dusk came in Australia, it didn't hang around, darkness fell in minutes, Scottish sunsets on the other hand, were the best in the world (the only trouble is, most times the sun forgets to rise again).

Willie parked up at his most favourite Cabrach view, looking out over Upper Cabrach croft to the 'Buck o' the Cabrach', a view he would never tire of as it changed its persona nearly every day. He stood, thinking, remembering how his grandfather talked about the large family who grew up at the now derelict croft, and how the children walked the three miles to and from school each day.

Willie was surely a man of roots, firmly embedded in the Cabrach heartland; he adored the place.

'One day,' he thought, 'I'm going to build a house here. What a great place to raise my kids - if I have any.'

That got Willie thinking about romance - he needed a girlfriend in his life. At twenty-six, maybe it was time to consider the possibilities. His life plan was unfolding as he scanned the horizon of the distant Aberdeenshire hills, daydreaming about his future.

'Married at thirty, two children, and possibly brewer by thirty five, manager at forty, and retired at fifty five, on a healthy company pension. If it pans out like that, I reckon I'd be a pretty contented guy,' thought Willie.

"So to make it happen, I'll need to start doing something about it," he pondered to himself. "I wonder where Friday night's dance is? Carron, Aberlour, Keith, or the Craig? Edinvillie, Archieston or Rothes? Keep it local and I've a better chance o' meeting a girl whose dad works in a still. And if she's nice, I'll be well in wi' her parents, as I'm a still man!" the scheming Willie mused.

3

Friday evening, and Willie's game plan got underway. He'd seen a poster in the Dufftown chipper. 'Clockwork sandwitch' were playing Craigellachie hall, and he was on two to ten.

"A shower at the still, on wi' the glad rags, and straight doon to the Craig for ten thirty!"

That was Willie free of distilling duties until Sunday

night on the 10pm to 6am shift. 'Clockwork sandwitch's' music was a bit on the heavy side for Willie's liking, but it was danceable. All the usual faces were there: Ronnie, Bob, Willie's sister Liz with her fiance Ian, their friends, and a host of other acquaintances eager to bring some night life to the Craigellachie hall. Not every dancing fan had the luxury of arriving at the hall in their own car like Willie. The final leg of their journey to the dance for most was usually by bus, organised by the dance promoters, but prior to reaching the bus's departure point, several revelers cycled from their outlying country homes to the edge of town, leaving their bikes neatly hidden for the journey home.

Cycling eight, ten miles there, and the same back home was the norm, but depending on the degree of alcohol intake before, during, and after the dancing, the cycle journey home could prove to be interesting. Sometimes before their roller coaster cycle ride, if they'd got lucky with a local girl, and did the honour of seeing her home, it could mean missing the bus back to base, resulting in a three mile walk from Craigellachie to Rothes, Craigellachie to Aberlour, not so bad at one mile, but Craigellachie to Dufftown is five miles, and at four on a Saturday morning, after a weeks work, and an evening of drinking and dancing, the uphill Dufftown walk home must've been a killer. Many's a Dufftown reveler was glad of Willie's unofficial taxi service.

4

Now heavily committed to shift work, Willie's social life was severely curtailed, he was restricted to only going out after finishing the two to 10pm shift every third week. He would have to get used to possibly missing some of his favourite annual Speyside events. Playing with the pipe band at the local highland games, camping over at Lonach, Tomintoul and Grantown, and of course playing in front of the Queen at the Braemar gathering. Life was changing for Willie, focusing on his distilling career was now his main consideration.

"Christ, I might even miss the Dufftown boys' ball. How can I get over this? I never miss the boys' ball."

Of all the highland games (even before he was piping in the band), he liked Aberlour's the best; there was just something special about the atmosphere. Was it the scenic riverside setting or just the general overall friendliness of the games that appealed, or maybe Aberlour has a unique quaintness in its portfolio of attractiveness.

"Yeah, but isn't Aberlour a bit of a one horse town," cracked the bitching Ronnie. "One distillery, one bakery, one butcher."

"No, no, that's Craigellachie you're speakin' aboot, Jimmy Crannas the horseman."

"Aberlour's quant, there's nothing pretty about Dufftown - well, maybe the old road bridge at Glen Ochtie or the castle, or the view from the golf coarse. Okay I take it all back, Dufftowns got charm as well. Just listen to us, you'd think we'd had a skinful, nae just two pints."

Stopping in past the 'Stalkers Rest' for a relaxing drink was something of a rarity for Willie. His free time was usually spent lounging at home in front of the telly, or taking his beloved car for a spin. Dufftown to Tomintoul, onto Grantown, and home via the scenic road to Knockando, stopping in past for coffee at fellow still man Alan Grant's house at Tomdoo. One of three distilleries at

Knockando, (all with a healthy reputation in the Speyside malt stakes), Tomdoo was a particular favourite of Willie's dad's. With nearly forty years of sampling experience behind him, John Thompson knew a good dram.

Like Willie, Alan had started work at Tomdoo straight from leaving school. Even though he was a few years older than Willie, and had been a still man for about eight years, he'd no ambition to climb the career ladder.

"I'll maybe change stills sometime, but I'll eywis be a still man, till I retire."

"Well, you ken fit yer deein."

Alan was the complete home bird, Had Willie asked him to go for a run in the Mini Cooper, he would've just said, "Fit for, there's things tae dee at hame, an' I'm on again at ten onyway." If Alan had lived in the Yorkshire Dales, or the valleys of South Wales he would have kept homing pigeons, he was that kind of guy. Maybe nae a whippet owner, but definitely pigeons.

How or why Willie and Alan had become pals was unusual to say the least, they were totally different kinds of people. Willie was friendly and outgoing, eager to get on with his life, and Alan was dull, inward thinking, boring, and lived a depressive existence to the same daily routine every week of every month of every year. Living at home in the row of distillery houses with his parents, every domestic whim was catered for, by his mum, Margaret. Life as a distillery shift worker's mum or wife would be totally governed by shift times. Preparing meals for the men folk would often be at unusual times of the day. Breakfast on the early shift, five thirty am, breakfast on the afternoon shift, eight to nine am, and on the night shift, two pm, after having slept all morning. The majority of distillery wives and mums were happy with their lot, accepting that, like farmers and fisher folk, distilling was a way of life, but of the three professions their men had the least demanding occupation.

With perks, such as a free company house, a three minute walk from work, and a complimentary bottle of whisky each month (replacing the daily staff drams), it was easily seen that working for a distillery company was one of the jobs to have in the nineteen seventies.

There had once been a rumour that Alan was seen on a day trip away from Knockando to Aberlour, but finding someone to verify the statement in Aberlour was proving very difficult. He had been spotted at Knockando Station, but those who knew him best said he was only looking for return journey tickets for his collection. Alan's world stopped at upper Knockando post office - and then only when the lower Knockando office had run out of postage stamps.

Alan never had any need to visit the outside world, as his mum and dad's living room housed the latest of television sets, and when he wasn't working, or sleeping, was glued to the twenty two inch screen. Every meal time, Alan sat with a tray on his lap, ogling whatever program was on, and laying the tray next to him on the couch, for his mum to remove, when she came through from the kitchen, to ask him if he wanted a cup of tea. Being an only child, Alan was spoilt beyond belief. From an early age, Alan had every toy his heart desired, and with his dad keen to get him into a job at Tomdoo, Alan never tried very hard at school, either academically or socially. If the seed of good standards are not sown early in life, the crop you reap will have little substance.

At thirty Alan was heading for bachelorhood. It had been five years anyway since he'd been to any of the local hall dances. The Knockando hall shindig was a ten minute cycle ride from Tomdoo, and when finishing his two to ten shift the smart alec Alan would turn up still dressed in his distillery dungarees and boots. Maybe once was funny, but because he got a laugh the first time he repeated himself every time he showed up at a dance in Aberlour, Carron or Archieston, and became socially wearisome. As he couldn't think of anything else that might be funny, he eventually stopped turning up, and a huge sigh of relief swept over the local girls. Since getting the message, Alan retreated back to his mum's couch never to darken the door of any local village hall again. By all accounts it looked like the older Alan was becoming the more his world was shrinking. In total contrast, Willie's world was growing and expanding at an accelerated pace. He knew exactly which direction he wanted his game plan course to take, and where he wanted to be at thirty, forty, and fifty, and at fifty five, financially secure, playing golf every day at his leisure.

5

Yet another close season came and went, and as the nights were drawing in Willie, the racketeer of romance, found himself circling another village dance floor, scanning the small clumps of girls bopping their way through the live band's numbers.

"Ronnie," shouts Willie, "I want to dance wi' the girl in the denims and brown boots, she looks classy, you take her mate."

They say that the first three minutes when meeting a

stranger are the most important, but with Willie, in this instance, it was the first three seconds. Everything happened, the eye contact, the smile, the body language, (and what a body). He knew immediately which handbag in the pile was hers. This girl was special: sandy coloured shoulder length hair, greeny, grey, bluish eyes, and she had all her own teeth. Love was a possible consideration this time, as Willie was in the 'finding a mate market'.

Securing the third dance was always the trickiest, if she stays and chats with you and dances the third dance, you're in with a chance, so you better have your patter ready, just in case 'tonight's the night'. There were two hurdles to clear if you were gonna be lucky at the end of the night, and see the girl home, and by getting the third dance Willie had safely cleared hurdle number one. To safely clear hurdle number two, and get the last dance of the night, you had to make sure your intended's dancing buddy had another group of friends to join up with, otherwise the signals become hazy and undecipherable.

Charming as ever, Willie's signals were clear and bold, and it was looking good for the last dance. The love gods were on his side as he extracted this damsels address.

"Well, you'll need a lift home then," prompted Willie. As always, that evergreen favourite 'Save The Last Dance for Me' filled the hall, hearts, and minds of the young romantics who were present.

Another romance was germinating (and nearly taking root) in an up-country dance hall, adding to the hundreds that have flourished down through the generations of Speyside life. Willie's Mini Cooper sat purring, eagerly awaiting to transfer its passenger and driver from hall to whatever address rendered. To Willie's great relief his trapee, Pamela was her name, lived on a farm somewhere between Carron and Archieston, and wasn't a toony. As the wee small hours crept up to five am, it was time for the romantic liaison to unhook, and get some sleep. A further date was arranged for the following week, and the mini cooper raced off to its garaged bed in Dufftown.

6

Two years of country courting later, saw Willie and Pamela making plans, and setting a date for their wedding. A modest family gathering, nothing too flash with a service at Knockando Church, and the reception for family and friends in the Lour Hotel, Aberlour. The practical-thinking Willie knew the score: if marriage and children were to be his life he knew that as soon as children arrived there would be no spare money in the family budget for anything else. Now was the right time to acquire the plot of land at his dream location, and build a family home. The pressure was on, saving for a wedding and building a house. Willie needed to work all the overtime available to him. Extra shifts, filling in for colleagues, cleaning days, and even cutting the distillery grass, all added to the savings account.

Like Willie, Pamela was brought up in a farming environment, although Pamela's dad's farm was more arable and productive than the barrenness of the Cabrach. It was a freehold of three hundred and fifty acres mainly growing barley for the distilling industry, which gave the family a very healthy standard of living. The Grant family were third generation to farm at the 'Crook o' Carron', and Pamela's brother David ran the unit with his dad, while Pamela worked at the Bank of Scotland in Aberlour. Mum

Margaret ran farmhouse bed and breakfast, mainly for the lesser-healed salmon fishers who couldn't afford the more sumptuous surroundings of the Craigellachie, Rothes Glen, or Dowans Hotels. Situated on the banks of the Spey, its location was an ideal getaway-from-it-all spot, tucked in behind a wooded area of silver birch, and catching the last rays of sunshine glinting on the salmon pools. A world away from the concrete jungle of the hard nosed business types daily lives who came to fish and relax.

The Grants were continually turning down ludicrous offers from the city slicers to buy the two farm cottages that stood adjacent to the farm road.

"Na, na," was Jock Grants reply, "My loon'll need een fin he gets merriate, an the ither een we'll jist dee up fir rentin oot, so they're nae fir sale.|"

Jock Grant was a big man, six foot two in his tackity boots, who lived and breathed farming. His grandfather had come down Speyside from Grantown to farm at the Crook o' Carron nearly a hundred years before, when buying a descent sized farm didn't break the bank. Jock's grandfather was an ambitious man, but Jock was eager to be just as ambitious, and couldn't sleep some nights for thinking out and planning how to make more money. At a family meal he'd put his plan in front of the family receiving full and enthusiastic backing,

"Why don't we get another farm?" said Jock. "And grow twice as much barley, but not with twice the work, we'll get in contractors"

And so Jock Grant rented an arable rich, flat as a pancake, combiners dream farm in the low lying Laich o' Moray.

"We'll winter the sheep there, an grow as much cereal

as possible. Mair grist tae the bankers mill!". The laughing Jock Grant was confident and happy he had his family's backing for his plan.

7

Wintertime in the Laich was always a few degrees less cold than up Speyside, even just the short distance of twelve to fifeteen miles nearer the Moray coast made all the difference. Travelers on the A96 have related their disbelief as they leave Fochabers in reasonable conditions but when you get to the top o' the dramlachs, it's a freezing winter white out, an' as far as Keith goes 'whit a cauld hole o' a place'. These people, of course, have only stopped in Keith to use the toilets in Fife Keith square, they have never experienced the genuine friendliness of it's inhabitants. For a well-seasoned traveller it would be very difficult to find another four thousand population, where the time of day is passed with such vigour.

The town of Elgin which is populated to five times the size of Keith, has a cold edge to it, unlike the friendly town, more akin with a city, perhaps it thinks its the Edinburgh of the north. But the surrounding farming land is second to none. Farmers who want to have well endowed bank accounts work on the Laich o' Moray land, but the price they pay for the privilege can be costly if they overstretch their elastic band.

Whereas a Banffshire farmer would be more inclined to say "If ye hiv it tae spend, ye hiv it tae spend," Jock Grant would milk the best of both worlds, he was a pure Speyside man who thrived spiritually in such a unique river valley, and saw the Laich ground purely as golden fields of barley for selling to the makers of the golden nectar. The hard working Grant family was a credit to the clan. Many branches of the Grant clan have done well in the business game, especially those who built or bought distilleries. There must be something in the Grant clan genes that bring success and fulfillment, and here was Willie Thompson, a loon fae a Cabrach croft dating a Grant (some guys hiv a' the luck!).

The Speyside valley reeks of character, from the Spey's rise in the Cairngorm through its sixty mile journey into the Moray Firth, there is an over abundance of cosy little neuks, bends in the river, that pass through a country lovers heaven. Craggy old Scots pine forest, a variety of broad leafed deciduous woodlands, plantations of forestry spruce in neat regimental lines. Silver birch and Larch line the riverbank, every mile holds a different view. A dream ticket would be to travel the Spey's course in a leisurely manner, absorbing the river's atmosphere, and perhaps stopping off at distilleries en route to sample their spirit (maybe only visitors to the area would be likely to pursue this treat as distillery workers can be very territorial).

8

The way to spot a distillery worker and his wife in a supermarket? (Apart from the S.M.D dungarees.) Their trolley's full of frozen meals, cheddar cheese, and bread for the sandwiches, and definitely no alcohol products in sight. After the abolishment of the courtesy drams, distillery companies (along with the free bottle) offered staff the opportunity, once a month, to purchase their wares at well below retail prices. Malt whisky in particular was termed, 'a best buy' and many Speyside drinks' cabinets bulged and creaked, straining with the amount of employees' purchases. It is rumoured that furniture shop owners in Keith grew wealthy on the sales of drink cabinets alone. If you were 'nouveau riche' in Speyside you had to have the aptly named 'cocktail cabinet' to display your vast array of drinks.

Distillery shift workers were a breed apart from the warehouse staff; they were men of impeccable routine with four pairs of dungarees, and at least one fresh polo shirt per day in their wardrobe. They were dedicated men to their job of producing their distilleries' unique tasting dram. Warehousing staff on the other hand lead a less regimented working life, and seem more relaxed for it. (or was it the frequent drams and the continuous whisky aroma in the warehouses that did it?). Warehouse staffs stress levels only rise when they are involved in spirit smuggling.

Jock Grant was curious, and was keen to ask Willie if much smuggling went on.

"Whit's the best whisky you've tasted Willie?"

"Well, there wis a butt, filled in '49. the lads would never leave it alone, even the still cat lapped it up. Christ knows what they're gonna dee when it histae ging oot!"

The still cats other delicacy was half a buttery twice a week. Butteries, that north east of Scotland phenomenon, are the world's best ice breaker. If you're introducing yourself in northeast Scotland, take along half a dozen and you'll make friends for life. Distillery shift workers could get fresh butteries on their way to work at any hour. It's nae that the butteries were straight oot o' the oven, it's just that butteries never go stale (an' that's without any preservatives). Folk in the Cabrach crofts had a dresser drawer full o' butteries, carrying on from the tradition of a dresser drawer o' porridge.

If you think that sounds like the folk o' the Cabrach are hardy, well there's folk in Glenlivet who can keep six ferrets doon their trooser legs for twenty minutes - an they're just the wimen. It's also been known for them to eat their butteries raw - well, fit wiy waste time bakin' them when they taste just as good havin' nae seen an oven?

"In your ten years at Glen Dufftoun, Willie, you must've seen some pretty cute smugglin. Well whit aboot the guys that have been a' their working days in the warehouse, they're the guys wi' the stories. The day will come though, when smuggling oot o' warehouses will be a thing o' the past. The guys will be too feart for their jobs, they'll hae too much to lose, a good wage, comfortable working conditions, free hoose, pension, and of course that free bottle. I think the best smuggling stories have definitely happened. Wouldn't it make a good read if you could collaborate all the smuggling stories in a book? Well you write it Willie, an' Mrs Grant'll sell it in the B an' B."

9

As harvest time and winter drifted past, and the Spey valley fields germinated with Spring crops, Willie and Pamela were still courting strong, looking forward to a summer holiday together during close season. A week in the Spanish or Italian sun took their fancy. Home came Pamela with the relevant brochures, phoning Willie right after her tea, but in her excitement, she'd got Willie's shift pattern wrong. He was on two to ten and nae ten to six, or six to two (nae wonder the quine was confused).

Ten past ten, Pamela's mum's phone rang and Willie and Pamela decided to meet the following Saturday to discuss where their holiday would be. The sun kissed beaches of Spain, or the olive palm groves of Tuscany, the arty architecture of Barcelona, or the picturesque shores of Lake Garda. Venice got the vote over Madrid, but the Spanish costas were beating the Dolomite foothills.

"Let's toss a coin, or will we go to Canada to visit your auntie and uncle in Vancouver?" Willie was getting a bit hacked off. When he'd gone on holiday wi' his mates, he recalled the decision on their destination as instant. This was a different ball game, here a woman had to make up her mind, and Willie was quickly finding out that that's something that can take a while. (Secretly he was thinking, 'If I ask her to marry me, how long will it be before I get an answer?').

But as Willie was mulling over the thought, Pamela sprang into action,

"Did you say Vancouver? Are you serious?"

"Well if you fancy it, we should go to Canada," says Willie with a huge grin on his face. As ever, since he was a young boy in the Cabrach he daydreamed about visiting Canada. The Rockies, The huge lakes, the red Indian culture, logging and lumberjacks. Every picture book he took home from the school library was a reference to Canada, and now this was the perfect opportunity to explore his dream.

Carefully working out the time difference, an excited Pamela phoned her auntie and uncle in Vancouver, and that weekend they paid the deposit for their first trip together. Only another two months of shifts, and Willie would get a long lie in the mornings, then its West in the big silver bird to the country of his dreams, with the girl he loves for the holiday of a lifetime.

"Aye you'll like Canada Willie," said Pamela's dad, "Mrs Grant an' me went oot for a holiday aboot five or six years ago. I've a brother in Alberta, you should look him up when you're over. He's got a spread there wi' a thoosan' steers. He went oot efter the war, and has done really well. We're struggling' here wi' oor subsidies while they ride the range a'day pretendin' to be cowboys."

"Sounds like a great life," said Willie, maybe Pam an' me will come back fae holiday and feel like we'd want to emigrate there, make moonshine, an' fish for sockeye salmon on lake Louise." Paradise, Willie, paradise.

Countin' down the weeks, Pam and Willie set about planning their itinerary, with a glass of wine, and Pam's mother's atlas spread across the ample pitch pine kitchen table.

Uncle Jim's spread on the banks of Little Smoky River would be their first port of call. Landing at Edmonton airport, it would be a three-hour drive Northwest to the ranch, staying a few days there before taking in the Calgary stampede, and catching the train through the Rockies to Vancouver.

"We don't need to do the Rockies' run in one go, we could stop half way and stay a couple of nights in a log cabin on the banks of the Colarado river, which is just like bein' in a fishing hut at Daluiane."

"Willie you've got some imagination, to listen to you, you'd think you'd already been there."

"Well Pam, it's just a' these years at the still, dreamin' on shifts, especially night shift. God help you if you fell asleep, but there's nae law against dreamin',".

“It sounds like a fantastic holiday,” said an excited Pam. “And it’s only eight weeks away. I’ll bet you can’t wait, Willie, to buy a pair of cowboy boots and a Stetson! My mum’ll iron your two favourite checked shirts, and off we go to ride the prairies.”

CHAPTER SIX

CALGARY AND BEYOND

1

A holiday together is a good thing for a couple's relationship, exposing to each other their mannerisms, moods, warts and all. The times when your body is in control of your brain, when holding your knife and fork incorrectly could mean instant separation. Spending all day (and night) together could be the first time in his life Willie realises that woman fart, and the first time for Pamela to find out that it's not only her dad who snores.

Final holiday check complete, the couple embarked on the first leg of their three-week Canadian odyssey, Dufftown to Dyce to Heathrow. Their first Canadian destination was Toronto, to visit a fellow piper Willie had befriended a few years previously at the Dufftown games when the Toronto pipe band had been on a highland tour. Willie recalled a tale he'd heard that pipers were the king of musicians, playing their way round the world with only a handful of tunes, and a good Glengarry to collect the busking money. He promised himself that one day he would dearly love to put the tale to the test, but this was a holiday with his girlfriend not an experiment in wanderlust survival. Next leg of the journey, Toronto to Edmonton, then Uncle Jim Grant's ranch, down to the Calgary stampede, and then through the Rockies by train to Vancouver.

On approach to Toronto International Airport, the CN tower with the revolving restaurant was the first visible landmark to catch Pam's long, wide eyed gaze. Pamela had won the coin toss at Heathrow for the window seat on the outward journey, and was thoroughly enjoying the thrill of descending from thirty thousand feet in preparation for landing. It was Pam's first long haul flight, all her other airplane journeys were short hops to Italy and Spain with her pals on budget flights. This flight was the real deal. Banking round for their approach Pam was gripping Willie's hand in a blood sapping vice lock, and Willie's thinking, 'If she holds onto our money wi' a grip like that, I've nothing to worry about'.

Safely on land, they were happy about being in Canada, but were taken aback by the forthright attitude of the passport man and his firm questions.

"Why are you in Canada? Where are you staying? How long are you staying for?"

It wasn't like this in Italy or Spain, and Pam was slightly shaken by his abruptness. "If we get him on the way back, I'm gonna tell the Sunday Post about him, an that'll teach him to be so rude."

"Calm doon, Pam we're on holiday in Canada, the best country in the world. You need a drink, and it'll hae tae be Canadian Club - when in Rome drink Rome cos they havnae heard o' Glen Dufftown here. First things first, let's get a map o' Canada and have a look at all those state names that turn us on so much, Ontario, Manatoba, Montana,

Wyoming, Saskatchewan, Alberta, Colarado. Names that conjure up pictures of wide-open spaces that go on forever, blue lakes surrounded by tall conifers, a log cabin with a smoking chimney on the banks of a Salmon River. Yeah, Pam, it's just like home but bigger." Willie was laughing

With a Canadian map purchased, the couple set off in search of a muffin break. Pam's mum and dad had raved about muffin breaks right to the day of departure, so Pam and Willie knew they couldn't go home to Banffshire without experiencing a muffin break. Now was as good a time as any, and so off they went in search of one of Canada's famous muffin break coffee houses. Within five minutes they were munching their way through the world's biggest muffins, and washing them down with the foamiest of cappuccinos, and musing over their forthcoming journey from Toronto to Edmonton.

"Wouldn't it be great to have three months off work, and take a campervan from East to West Coast of Canada, and also coast to coast of America? Just think, we could even visit Bob Dylan's home town, Hibbing in Minnesotta, and loads of other mysterious place names like Stillwater, Siox Lookout, Devils Lake, Thief River Falls, Fargo, Cheyenne Pass, Moose Jaw, Saskatoon, Buffalo Park, and Medicine Hat. That would be fantastic, Pam, I could save up my holidays and get two months off at one go."

"Aye, that's a great idea," agreed Pam. "If we really enjoy this holiday we should seriously consider that for the next time. Right now we need to contact your piping pal Rob, to see if he can meet us somewhere in the city centre, so that we've got a bed for tonight."

Piping pal Rob was Robert McKinnon, born on the banks of Lake Ontario in the town of Belleville, moving to

Toronto to gain university education, and now works for Canadian Club.

"Well Pam, that's what he told me anyway, he got the job when he was piping a visitation of Japanese to Toronto. He thought of being a mounty a while, but his bag pipe playing must've scared the horses, so he joined the club sorta speak." Full of fun,

Willie always had to have a laugh so he tried out his favourite Canadian joke on Pam. "Did you hear about the Scotsman travelling through Canada with his tour guide?"

"No, Willie."

"Well, they were high in the Rockies when they came to a clearing in the Cedar forest and were confronted by a huge deer stag-like beast. 'What the hell's that?', asked the Scotsman. 'It's okay', said the guide, 'it's only a moose'. 'Jesus, if that's the size o' your mice, I'd hate to see a rat', said the flummoxed Scotsman."

That fair tickled Pam's fancy, so to keep the keep the momentum going, Willie recounted a story about when he used to keep up his fitness for his football career by going out jogging most days, usually a couple of hours before his shift at the distillery started. His favourite jog was a four mile route that took him past Glen Dufftown's barrel yard, where thousands of empty barrels were stacked before being called upon for filling. A few times on a run before his 10pm to 6am shift Willie caught sight of a local worthy helping himself to the billans in the bottom of the barrels. The worthy would fill up two plastic gallon containers, and stagger off between the rows of casks seemingly happy with his night's haul. But one particular occasion while jogging past the barrel pile, he heard a distinctive moaning. Pausing for a breather, and peering through the dusky light he could see the whisky plunderer jammed in between two rows of casks lying on his back with his bounty gurgling onto the ground from his white plastic container. He'd obviously been sampling a little too much of his ill gotten gains, or (grains). These days, security men with dogs patrol distilleries' interests, but this was the seventies and a free for all. Down the years, thousands of gallons of bullins would've been strained several times through a pair of womans tights (for extra flavour), and enjoyed in homes and garden sheds throughout Speyside.

Before Willie could regale Pam with more of the same, a jovial six foot Canadian with a "Hi there, you Jocks!" appeared as if a meeting had been prearranged. "I'm here to see my mum an' dad off to sunny Florida, so we've got the house to ourselves! I just couldn't remember what flight you were on, but now I've got rid of my parents I can relax and get tanked up with you guys."

"Well," said Willie, "Let's start wi' the Glen Dufftown, I've got a couple o' bottles in our case, let's get to your pad and get the ice bucket out."

"Willie, if you've got the Scotch, I've got the rocks."

2

In fifteen minutes, they were all seated and relaxed in the spacious downtown Toronto apartment.

"So tell me, Willie, how did you come to be working in a distillery? The pay must be pretty good to come on holiday to Canada and it's nae even your honeymoon."

"Well if you pour a good sized Glen Dufftown, Rob, I'll tell you the story. It came fae third year at school, I'd said to my mum an' dad at tea time that the careers officer was coming to school next day, and they bandied about a few ideas. Joiner, sparky, fireman, joinin' the police, working' for the council... They had loads of ideas, but only when my dad suggested a distillery job like my uncle Bob did I kinda got a bit more enthused. Next day the careers officer's doing his talk, and going round the class asking us individually what job we wanted to do when leaving school. I just said, 'I want to be a distillery manager'. I could hear a few gasps at my statement, but that's when I decided what I was gonna aim for."

"That was pretty decisive. Great forethought for only being fourteen years old. Are you going to get there?"

"I think it's possible, I may have to change companies to do it, but I should get there with determination and a bit of luck."

"Did you pass any exams or go to university or that?"

"No, Rob, just left school wi' two o levels and started work in the warehouse squad at Glen Dufftown after close season nineteen sixty. I will need to make it to manager by the time I'm forty so that I'm on the full pension, and I can then retire at fifty. But that's enough shop, tell us what you've got lined up for us in Toronto. We've got two days before we're on that big silver bird to Edmonton."

At that moment, Pam's penny dropped, she could instantly conjure up a complete picture of her future, a future that seemed as sound as a pound.

"We'd like to see an ice hockey match Rob, like The Toronto Tigers verses The Winnipeg Wonders, or The Montreal Masters, against The Hudson Bay Hardliners. Pam's needin' to see a mounty, but maybe they're only unique to Montreal, and you've got real bobbies in the rest of Canada."

3

In the blink of an eye Pam and Willie were boarding their flight to Edmonton, for the next leg on their Canadian odyssey. Canada was Willie's dream world, Willie's kind of country, for years he had dreamed of visiting its shores. In his younger days, every book he could get his hands on about the country was 'grist to the mind of knowledge'. The remoteness, the rugged landscape, waist deep snow, log cabins with smoking chimneys, and only bears and beavers for company. These were the dreams of a man brought up in the Cabrach, where the ruggedness of the territory was where the similarity ends.

The Canada Willie and Pam were visiting was full of sophistication, only a stones throw from the American border, the land where the dollar in your pocket is the value of your freedom. The most affluent society of modern times, and mainstream Canada was only a yard behind.

When Willie used to sit on the dry stane dykes of his corner in the Cabrach, listening to skylarks, peeweeps, and black cock, he visualised pictures of Canada's outback. But as soon as the Cabrach winter descended, and the snow drifts were halfway up the window frames of the croft house, the dreaming stopped. Such was the harshness of the Scottish winter, the full time objective was to keep warm and survive until the bleating of newly born Spring lambs heralded a warmer season. Surviving Cabrach winters for humans and animals alike is a tough ride. Extra layers of clothing are needed to keep out the chilling wind that whistles o'er the 'buck' (the only Cabrach hill over 2400 feet). It's essential that your outer garment has a lined hood, and in the coldest of the winter you also need a woolen tammy to help keep up your body temperature. It's the kind of place that's heaven in summer and hell in winter, and if you weren't born and bred in the district and wanted to settle there, it's unlikely you'll stay longer than your first winter. Dufftown winters can be long and cold but nothing near as endless as the exposed Cabrach winters. Cabrachites are a hardy breed, maybe because they have their own private supply of Glen Dufftown piped to their homesteads from a secret still in the glen, giving them extra insulation.

Willie and Pam's flight taxied to a halt at Edmonton airport and waiting to greet them were Pam's uncle George and her cousin Craig.

"Are you folks ready for Canada? Well, yup, Canada's sure ready for you! A coupla hours up the highway, we'll be home at the spread. Are folk still eatin' them small steaks in Dufftown?"

Pam's uncle never stopped for a breath, and Willie was getting the impression uncle George was keen to let him and Pam know that since settling in Canada he had done very well for himself and his family. Being proud of your achievements is one thing, but down right boastfulness is loathsome, and when it comes over without any humour or panache, it's just tedious and boring. Two or three days at the ranch with uncle George would be enough for Willie, and then the Calgary stampede would be imminent. Calgary was a six-hour train ride, and both Willie and Pam were relieved to be hearing the clickety clack in their ears as the long snake like train trundled on South.

"Definitely in Calgary, Pam, I'm buyin' cowboy boots and a Stetson, I won't ride the rodeo, but I'm gonna get boots - we both should. Aye, if there's anywhere in Canada to be a cowboy, it's got to be Calgary".

Deep into the darkness of the Canadian night, on and on the diesel train rumbled, Pam with her copy of 'The visitors guide to Canada', and Willie dropping off to sleep dreaming of his cowboy boots. If you were a lover of the old Wild West, and the relatively new Hollywood version, Calgary was the place to see. It had more cowboys, and cowgirls per square metre than a Dufftown joiner has feet on his three-foot rule. Rugged, muscle bound dare devils (and they were just the woman) strut their stuff at the rodeo for the thousands who visit, and can become cowpokes for a day, perfecting the tamer skills of the ranch hands.

With the daytime rodeo thrills safely lassoed, the nightlife in Calgary was imminent. Willie had his boots and Stetson bought and ready, Pam settled for just the boots, and they were now for proving they were as country as any west American couple who liked country rock. Down town they rode in their taxi to the best tourist honky tonk in town, for some great singalong country standards, Pam had sung in local shows at Knockando hall, Archieston, and Carron, and could hold a country melody easier than pullin' on her cowboy boots.

"Yip Pam, I'd sure like to go to Montana, where the millionaire cowboys live, but I'm just a Dufftown still man, and I suppose we'll have to do with Calgary an' Vancouver."

"Willie you're never satisfied, just be happy you're in Canada."

"Yeah, Pam, it's just me dreamin' again, this Canada's fine for me, Montana can wait until our next visit."

4

Vancouver, gateway to the Pacific, a fusion of cultures,

simmering in the melting pot of life. Pam was reading from the in-flight magazine, and Willie, well he was in cowboy heaven admiring his boots,

"I canna wait to walk doon Balvenie street in these babies."

"Oh, for goodness sake Willie, it's nae like they're gonna be the only cowboy boots to walk the streets o' Dufftown! Dozens o' Americans visitin' the still have been wearin' them for years."

"I ken, but Pam, they never see Dufftown, they get bussed into Glen Duffers car park, and bussed away again to Baxters without ever settin' foot up the street."

"My cowboy boots will be the only resident pair for miles around."

"Fair enough, Willie, just dinna wear them when you're oot playin' wi' the pipe band."

"Oh Pam, look what the name o' the in flight film is called - 'Midnight Cowboy'/ I'm definitely watchin' that."

After an excellent in-flight dinner, Willie settled himself to watch the film while Pam got comfortable and drifted off for a couple of hours' sleep. One of the top films of the seventies, staring Dustin Hoffman and Jon Voight, Midnight Cowboy told the story of a young country stud arriving in New York, and befriending a city tramp from the seedier side of life. With a dialog and soundtrack to die for, it certainly was one of the cinematic classics.

After the film finished and the cabin lights went back up to normal brightness, Capt. Chuck Robertson announced touch down at Vancouver airport to be fifty minutes away, and gave a short weather briefing to his two hundred or so passengers. The late afternoon flight would touch down at five twenty, and waiting to drive Pam and Willie to the

North Vancouver suburb of North Delta would be Pam's uncle and aunt John and Elsie Grant. Married at Auchbreck Church, Glenlivet in 1946, they immediately emigrated to British Columbia when John replied to an advert for lumberjacks to work in the great logging camps of North West British Columbia. Accessible only by seaplane, the camps were like small cities doted along the coast, and were home to John and Elsie for thirty years. Now fifty, John was pensioned off, and the couple was living the idyllic suburban life style of the retired.

The Speyside couple's first view of Vancouver told them immediately this was a city on the coast where every second or third inhabitant was the owner of a weekend pleasure boat. Thousands upon thousands of them tied up in neat pontoons as far up the coast as the eye could see. Vancouver was a modern city, a lifetime away from the country life of Calgary. If a cowboy walked down the street in Vancouver everyone would be thinking, 'What's he doin' so far North', then walk on and forget they ever saw him.

Canadians, cool and laid back, and Vancouver a widely cosmopolitan city (perhaps one of the world's most cosmopolitan per head of population), with ethnic groups of huge proportions in the deepest downtown areas. Being situated on the Pacific coast, it was a Shangri-La for Australasian travellers for over a hundred and fifty years. Sparkling with sunshine in the summer, knee deep in snow in the winter, but always alive and vibrant, Vancouver had a friendly buzz in its big heart. Pam and Willie knew all about snow, but Vancouver's was brittle and fluffy, not like the heavy dense stuff that hung around Dufftown's streets for six months of each year - which six months depended on which direction the wind whistled through the Conval hills. Dufftown snow was deep and depressingly wet, while Vancouver snow was light, dry and airy with the slopes of grouse mountain the skiers' playground.

Touch down, and Pam and Willie's first impressions of Vancouver were of a fresh clean city with a small town atmosphere.

"It's just like Edinburgh," said Pam, "but with more foreigners."

"I love the Red Indian references, it all seems to mix so well."

"I could see us living here Willie, it seems such a great place, only twenty minutes from the forests and mountains, what a place."

Willie was being silent, thinking: 'I love cowboy boots an' Stetsons, hunting and fishing, lakes and mountains, but I want to be a distillery manager, and there's nae' distilleries in Vancouver'.

Of the three Canadian cities she had visited on this trip, Vancouver was Pam's favourite; she'd fallen in love with it, and with her uncle and auntie having done so well, and seeming so happy, Pam felt this was the country and city for her.

"What like are the winters?", she asked Elsie,

"Oh they can be pretty cold, minus forty sometimes if the winds fae' the North."

"Minus how much?" asked Pam, a remark that left a different impression, leaving Pam a little speechless. "Gee, I thought Dufftown winters were cold, minus ten at their worst, maybe minus twenty once in a blue moon, but never forty! Jesus that's cold."

"But Pam it's a different kind of cold here, Scottish

winters are a wet cold, here's more crisp an' dry. It's a cold winter, but we always get a great summer when we go up to our cabin at Kamloops for a spot of fishing. There's nothing like hooking a sockeye salmon in full flight, cooking it over an open air log fire under a blanket of twinkling stars."

"What could be more romantic for a Scottish couple than that? You could do a lot worse than come and live in Canada."

Still Willie was quiet. He was thinking more Australia; yes, if there was to be a move away from Speyside, it would have to be Australia.

Willie broke his silence: "Pam, are the Dufftown winters nae cold enough for you? I like Canada fine, but to hell wi' the winters! Go to Australia and you can have summer all year round, ev'ry year. It's Australia for me if anywhere."

Willie's statement kinda took the wind out of an excited Pam's sails, and she remembered an exercise her mum and dad did when they were considering emigrating to Canada fifteen years previously. You need to write down your home country's good and bad points, and the good and bad points of the country you intend emigrating to. If your intended country has 50% more good points than the country you're living in, then you need to be emigrating.

"Australia can't be that good," says Pam, "'cause how come in the world rankings of best countries to live in, Canada always comes out top? In the Western world, Canadians enjoy the highest standard of living."

"That must be just in the Northern hemisphere Pam," retorts Willie/ "Australia's definitely best in the Southern hemisphere."

Conflict was brewing in the Thompson-Grant camp,

but Hope was at hand - the *town* of Hope! Only a few hours North East of the city, it was just the perfect distance to drive for a coffee and muffin break, and experience some real Canadian countryside.

Hope nestled at the foot of some hills that nestled at the foot of the Rockies, and was a pioneer-like town, a bit Davy Crocket. But the muffin break café was atmospheric with its heavy wooden beams, stuffed moose heads, gigantic log fire, and deep leather couches. It certainly wasn't the plastic 'cosy teapot' Dufftown, a place that's more shreek than chic.

Having filled themselves with the rocky mountain high, it was back to North Delta to rest their Stetson hats for the next day's adventure.

5

Up with the sun next morning, Willie was making jokes about needing to borrow uncle John's shovel to go and dig for whisky on Grouse mountain

"It's maybe nae the best dram available," said Willie, "but it's whisky. I'll get the cable car to drop me at the fillin' head, an' I'll soon be singin' that old favourite, 'We'll be dramin' round the mountain when we come'."

Another few days and their Canadian odyssey would be over, Willie an' Pam would be back to auld claes an' porridge, back to their jobs, and in a few weeks their holiday would become a distant memory. If Willie had learned only one thing about holidays and travelling, it was to make sure he lived in the moment.

CHAPTER SEVEN

THE PROPOSAL

1

The year was racing on and fast approaching Willie's twenty eighth birthday in October. Glenlivet harvests were baled but still sitting out in the fields. By this late in the season, Morayshire farmers are contemplating a start to their ploughing, but further up Speyside the farming cycle turns a little slower.

Not so in the distilling industry of the time: these were boom times, every Speyside mash tun, wash back, and spirit still were bubbling furiously twenty four hours a day, seven days a week. Distilling companies were stockpiling spirit, new warehousing complexes were springing up in locations several miles from where the spirit was being made. Bond warehousing was a massive operation on its own, totally separate from the spirit production. Such was the boom that brand new distilleries were also sprouting up, it seemed the world couldn't get enough whisky.

Willie was puzzled: "How could the new distilleries compete without going bankrupt? Build a £1,000,000 distillery, and have to wait eight years to sell your product, is that nae' commercial madness? But I suppose every industry has its mavericks," said a bemused Willie.

"Och the high heed yins ken whit they're dein," replied Willie's dad. "They've got it a' worked oot, let them worry aboot the money, an we'll dee the work. It's bin that wiy since time began, an' it'll be the same hunners o' 'ears fae' noo'." John Thompson was a practical man, from his cap and donkey jacket right down to his steel toe capped boots.

"So you an Pam are getting' on fine are ye? We'll ken when it cams tae' meetin' her parents if she's the one. Is that the wiy o' it?"

Willie's dad wis haein' a bit o' a giggle. Willie said nothing' and sped off in his Mini Cooper for Aberlour to meet Pam from her work, as they had planned a Chinese meal in Elgin, and a visit to the cinema. Willie had enjoyed 'Midnight Cowboy' on the Calgary to Vancouver flight, but it hadn't hit mainstream Scottish cinemas yet, so they were going to see 'The Day of The Jackal' a tense edge-of-your-seat thriller, perfect entertainment for a courting couple, with the end result firmly locked in their minds.

2

It was unusually mild for December, with Christmas only two weeks away, and romance was in the air. On the road back up country, Willie pulled over into their favourite lay by on the banks of the Spey, and with no messing about, or fumbling around for words, he asked Pam if she'd marry him.

Pam immediately replied: "Yes, of course I will, Willie. I love you dearly! I've been hoping you would ask me soon. I was thinking on holiday you were going to ask, especially that night in the country bar in Calgarry, you just seemed so happy, maybe it was the beer!"

"What about telling our parents?"

"Jings, they haven't even met yet, we better organize that this weekend, perhaps Sunday tea at the farm."

"Great Pam, that'll be fine, I'll tell my mum an' dad tonight."

"Aye dinna tell them we're engaged, leave that for a surprise at Christmas, that'll give us time to get a ring."

"Great thinking Pam, I'm just relieved you said yes!"

A late harvest moon shimmered on the fast flowing water as it raced past their feet, and a light shower of rain made the fishing hut's felt roof glisten in the low light.

"This would be a good spot for writing poetry or composing songs, Pam. It's a pity I'm a piper and nae a musician."

The setting of Pam's proposal and acceptance was world beating. They were maybe just an average Banffshire couple, but the moment was world class, and they were living and loving every second of it.

3

John and Mary Thompson arrived for Sunday tea at three in the afternoon. Pam and Willie greeted them at the door.

"Come on in and meet my mum an' dad. I'll take your coats," said Willie.

The Grants were in the kitchen, Pam's dad was sitting at the AGA in his slippers, reading the Sunday Post, and mum was keeping an eye on the ginger cake she was baking in the AGA's oven.

"Will we just sit here or will we ging through, mam?" asked Pam's dad.

"Oh, we better ging through tae the soft seats, I've got the fire on, Aye, c'mon through folks," said mum Grant. "It's affa fine tae meet you both, Pam has told us so much about you."

"Well, oor Willie kept mentioning this girl Pamela Grant to us, so we thought there must be something to it."

The good room at Sharny Dubs was very cozy, and warmly decorated with flock wall covering (a little more up market than your average wood chip), deep floral patterned three piece suite, with curtains to match. A sixties' screw in legs radiogram which doubled as a drinks display, sat against a mirrored wall; and behind the couch was an oak sideboard adorned with family photographs. On either side of the sideboard hung two paintings depicting Scottish farming scenes. Commanding the main position in the sweeping bay window was the latest twenty two-inch colour television set, the older model had been demoted to the kitchen. This was a farming family who enjoyed their comforts bought on the back of hard work in three hundred acres of Speyside farming land. The bulk of farming families spend most of their house time, either in the kitchen or in bed, but not the Grants, most evenings they were in their good room appreciating their comforts.

4

The company were making their way from the kitchen past a nineteen thirties' Scottish pine dresser through the hallway just as the six foot six tall grandfather clock struck four pm. Opposite the nineteenth century clock stood a twenties oak coat and umbrella stand, giving the hallway an elegant entrance to the house, unlike the back door which was cluttered with oil skins, jackets, hats, welly boots, and an assortment of shepherd's crooks.

Sunday tea at Sharny Dubs Farm was a very traditional farmhouse bill of fare, with an embroidered linen table cloth adorning a large oak dinning table which groaned under the grand array of pancakes, scones, oatcakes, cheeses, shortbread, current loaf, white baps and jam.

The dining room was a mixture of handed down antique heirlooms and fifties furniture, with the inevitable picture of a highland glen above the open coal fire. A mirrored sideboard with Mrs Grant's plate collection stood against the opposite wall, and draping the ample bay window were heavy burgundy velvet curtains. Normally a Sunday family tea would be taken on the kitchen table but this was a special occasion, and so out came the good china.

Mrs Grant served tea, and the freshly baked bannocks were goin' doon a treat.

"Div ye ken, Willie," said John Grant, "Pam has an affa appetite! Fin she leaves hame I'll jist hae tae grouw a' park o' neeps - an half an acre less tatties!"

"Oh, John," said Mrs Grant. "That's a bit exaggerated. John Jnr. took a bit o' feedin', Pam's just a slip o' a girl."

"Aye, like her mum," said John Snr., hoping to regain his popularity at the table.

5

The Thompsons thouroughly enjoyed their visit. After tea

the two Johns swapped farming tales, and the mums discussed their many achievements in the Keith show WRI tent over the years. Pam and Willie volunteered to do the washing up, then cuddled together on the kitchen couch to watch tv. A fitting end to the day that brought their parents together for the first time.

"What have you got planned for Christmas dinner, folks?"

"There will only be me an' John, Pam and John Jnr., unless he's planning to go to his girlfriends."

"Have you got something planned, or would you like to come to the farm here. You could easily stay over, we've got plenty space."

"That's an excellent idea, mum," said Pam.

That idea was agreed, which made sure that Pam and Willie's secret surprise would have the perfect location for announcing their engagement.

6

As Christmas approached, Willie had more good news in his basket. The offer he made for an acre of prime Cabrach building land had been accepted, and his house project could now begin. Prior to the Canadian holiday, he had held discussions with a local architect to draw up plans for a two-story house, and he was now anxious to look over the results. Having made an appointment with their architect, Willie and Pam were off to view the blueprint. They now had two surprises for their parents: a diamond ring, and a set of plans.

Like half the business world, the stills shut up shop for the festivities, and it gave Willie a chance to visit his house location, and plan exactly where on his piece of Scotland the house would be built.

He was thinking to himself: 'What a great way to start the New Year, building a house, and getting engaged. Could life get any better?'

And as he stood and gazed at the snow covered 'buc', he remembered his uncle in Australia's favourite saying, (usually when they were barbequed out, and onto the second flaggan of red wine): 'What are all the poor people doin' now?'. It kinda summed up a contented feelin' in Willie.

If the house build starts on time, and stays on track, by next Christmas Willie and Pam should be in their new home commanding the best view in Banffshire. Willie's Queens view looked out across the upper Cabrach from the gateway to Upper Cabrach croft sweeping towards the 'buc'. From his advantage point, Willie could see the croft he grew up in, and, scanning the territory, he felt a belonging to his roots. Willie had done a fair bit of travelling but was definitely a roots' person.

7

When it comes to start the house, his only outside assistance in the self-build would be the ground preparation and laying the foundations. All other work would be done by tradesmen friends on evenings and weekends.

"Aince the foonds are doon, we'll get crackin' wi' the dwarf was. How high's a dwarf wa Willie?"

"Oh, aboot yae high."

Willie was in conversation wi' his brickie. "Fan will I start, Willie?"

"Well, the plans should be through the council's planning office by early March. Then ye can get the foonds in, and you start in April efter a' the frosts oot."

"Aye, at'll dee jist grand."

"If I can start the jinner by June, the plumber and sparky by July or August time, we should be in and painting by October."

"That's the kinda timescale I'm looking at."

"Then you're getting merryade, are you?"

"Well, that's Pam's department, but I think we'll probably get hitched the following summer, and I'd like to honeymoon in Italy. Milan, Venice, Rome, yeah, an Italian honeymoon, that's what I'd like."

CHAPTER EIGHT

WILLIE'S CABRACH CASTLE

1

Mid March, and the postman delivered the approved plans for Willie's castle in the Cabrach. A two story, four bedroom, breeze block and sandstone construction. Willie's special feature in the house would be the upstairs lounge where he could sit and look out over his kingdom, sampling a few malts from his drinks' display, created from a varnished hoggy barrel.

Having done a rough costing of the house build, it was time for a detailed look at the prices of the materials he would need. He had secured a £15,000 loan from his bank, and was determined the project wouldn't go over budget. Willie sat down, proportioned the materials, and started the long slog round the suppliers for the keenest prices.

Winter's mantle was evaporating in the Cabrach, and a few early visitors were arriving in Dufftown.

"What's that smell?" asked the American on his approach to the still.

"Oh that's just the Joe," replied the guide.

"Gee, what was he eating last night?" said the Yank.

"No," said the guide, smirking at the American. "The Joe is the fermenting of the wash - sometimes known as the beer."

"So what happens in the local towns in your beautiful part of the world?" the American asked.

"Well in Burghead if they've had a rotten Christmas, they jump into the harbour on boxing day. And if that doesn't work, a couple of weeks later they try to burn a few folk wi' a thing called 'The Clavie'. In Stonehaven they swing fire balls roond their heeds, and in Shetland they burn their boats."

"Yip, the Scots were always a bit crazy, but they can sure make good whisky!"

Willie completed his house project homework just as the JCB he ordered to do the founds appeared over the brow of the hill, and immediately he was on the phone to his brickie for an April start. Summer was knocking on spring's door when Willie and his joiner pal Jim set about erecting the roof joists, ably assisted by Ronnie and Bob. The popular Willie had no shortage of helping hands, Jim was being paid for his skills while at this stage of the build, Ronnie and Bob were there for the crack, and a few cans of beer.

2

Approaching Dufftown on the Craigellachie road (the A941), on a crisp late December around teatime, you get a feeling of entering a different world. Once you climb the hill out of the forestry trees to the highest point before going downhill again, and look over the valley towards Dufftown, there is a sense of difference. It's perhaps the smoke flumes from the newly lit coal fires trying to outreach the flumes from fires that have been lit most of the day; or perhaps it's the aura of the angel's share drifting up from the warehouses.

Yes, there's definitely something in the air over pagoda city. Tibet and Japan may boast a few more pagodas per square mile, but the Dufftown ones are there for a more worthwhile reason; they represent the real meaning of spiritualism. A decent double Dufftown dram can help you meditate, and in some cases levitate. (Quick another dram, some of these monks are still awake).

On occasions, their 'hot' whisky from their hot water bottles would perish the rubber seal, and they would place orders for copper breastplates at an alarming rate, so much so that there was not enough spare copper for making arthritis wristbands for ten years.

Willie and Pam's house was taking shape, and looking like the grand structure they had planned.

"Does it nae look too big Willie, stickin' oot like a sare thumb on the moor side?"

"No, I dinna think so, Pam. By the time we plant a few semi mature trees round about, it'll be less obtrusive. Just look at the view. I canna wait to be in the upstairs lounge wi' the wood burner on, and enjoying a dram o' Dufftown. Pam it'll be magic."

"Yeah, Willie we're so lucky. We're realising our dream, and we're still in Scotland. Would it have been like this if we'd emigrated to Canada?"

"Probably. If building your own house is your bag, you'll do it wherever you are, and just because we're building a hoose here in the Cabrach doesnae mean we're here for ever."

3

Summer was on the wane when Bob the sparky was finishing the light fittings, and wi' the clocks goin' back the following weekend the race was on to get the rooms taped, emulsioned, and the wood burning stove lit before any early Cabrach frost descended. Willie was on two to ten, and managed four hours each evening, taping and rubbing down after his shift. Taping and rubbing down, no matter how large or small the house is, everybody who has done it knows that its the worst job in any house build or renovation. A few afternoons the following week straight from six to two would see the taping pretty near done, and then onto the painting. Drafting in parents, brothers and sisters, rolling on the emulsion would only take a weekend, and Willie made sure he had enough gear to get it done in one go.

With Willie's dad due to retire when next year's close season kicks in, it was in Willie's interest to keep his ear to the ground. Having proved himself sharp at his still man post and being the brewer's loon, he would definitely be in the running to take responsibility at dramin' the men. Two clearics a day and a broonic at five o'clock on a Friday was the regular procedure. To provide Friday's brown dram, it was the brewer and the warehouse foreman's responsibility to extract enough whisky from the warehouse that was to everyone's liking, and that included the manager, his cronies, the excise man, and the brewer's cliche. It could mean two or three discrete visits to the warehouse on a Friday, fitted in between keeping an eye on the men, and seeing to the paperwork for a consignment of whisky south. A slip up with the paperwork, and demotion would follow pretty swiftly: when you consider that one barrel of mature whisky is worth £2,000 before tax, getting the paperwork right would demand concentration. A fully laden artic lorry of mature whisky (how come they're called artic lorries? Did they all pass their road test in the artic?) must have been worth more than anything else on the A9 in them days, and none of them were ever ambushed. What an easy target, miles and miles of empty road, plenty time to roast the goose and get away, but it never happened. Just one lorry had on board enough whisky to sink all the boats in the Cooper Park and refill Harry Wills goldfish pond twenty times. For the amount of lorries that went down that road in a week from Speyside distilleries to the Glasgow bonds, and not one was ever high jacked, it's hard to believe.

4

The tattie holidays came, the time changed, and the weary couple watched the Dufftown bonfire fireworks from their back bedroom window, the final room to be emulsioned. Piece by piece over the next few days they moved in their smaller bits of furniture and the once empty house was beginning to look like the home they had planned a year before.

Willie was looking forward to Saturday evening coming round, so he could enjoy a celebration dram, and for once he wanted a low temperature to sweep over the Cabrach so he could test the wood burning stove's efficiency, and see if any adjustments were needed in the heating system. All day Saturday was spent with a borrowed van, moving in the bigger belongings, and nearing teatime as Willie had predicted, the air was getting colder, heavy frost was descending on the Cabrach. Pam was in her new kitchen rustling up a mean spaghetti bolognaise as the outside temperature dropped to one or two degrees. By the time Willie got home from returning the van, the bottle of red wine was at a cozy 18 centigrade, just short of room temperature, and the perfect evening was underway.

Willie was reminded that for the first time since he proposed over a year ago to Pam on the banks of the Spey, he and Pam had reached a milestone in achieving their first home together. With building the house parallel to working at his job, he hadn't thought anything about his achievement, so now was the occasion to pat himself on the back, and pour an extra large dram.

Each morning seemed sharper than the one before, winter was sinking its teeth into the Cabrach landscape, with the 'buck' under a two foot blanket of whiter than white snow. Steam rose from unregulated lines of silage throughout the farming community, as farmers' tractors chugged across frozen fields at walking pace. The hot breath from sheep and cattle evaporated silently skyward as they chomped and chewed their way through tons of winter-feed. Local Cabrach residents respected the harsh conditions that winter could bring and knew all about what to wear to keep out the cold. Four layers on top, three layers below, and when they went outside an extra jacket.

5

The next big event in Willie's life, was his wedding to Pam, and by the time the long cozy nights in front of the wood burner gave way to being outside after teatime working on building a garden, they had decided on a favourable date. Close season seventy-nine would be when they would tie the knot in Aberlour Parish Church, and have their reception in the Memorial hall, Dufftown. Willie would take three weeks holiday, a week before the wedding for any last minute arrangements, and then the two-week honeymoon in Northern Italy.

Pam set about planning their big day, and with only five months to July there no spare time to squander: dresses, cars, cakes, flowers, invitations, favours... Pam's list was growing by the hour, and Willie could see the depletion of his bank balance eb faster than a raging sea.

"Pam, we need to open an account for the wedding, and get a couple of grand into it." We'll save like mad and pay a few things as we go along so that when we come back from honeymoon we're nae faced wi' a heap o' bills to pay oot o' our first months wages. Payin' the mortgage on the hoose is pressure enough."

6

As the weeks sped past into months, Pam and Willie's wedding plans were well ahead with only the invitations sitting on the sideboard to be sent out.

June dawned, and a nervous Willie began to adopt commando tactics at the end of his shifts. Like the Burghead clavie crew, the blackening boys were a determined bunch. Dressed in their oldest clothes, prepared for a messy time, they would kidnap their victim, strip him or her to their underpants, then tar and feather them. Then they would parade them round the streets in whatever transport was available to them, usually a tractor and trailer.

As his shifts were finishing, Willie would check out the still tractor's location, and see if the trailer was hocked up, then stelfully leave his post and take an unscheduled route out of the still. Once he was on the Cabrach road he could relax, only at the still, or in Dufftown would he be ambushed.

Then, two weeks before the wedding, while on the two to ten, the assistant brewer called him to the brewers' office. Willie's guard was down, and crossing the yard fae the still hoose to the office his work mates pounced.

"The brewer jist wints to see fit time div ye pit o'er the wines. You're comin' wi' us!"

Caught and outnumbered ten to one, Willie had no choice but to surrender to his captors. Offering no resistance, Willie stripped off knowing he wasn't going to die of hypothermia as it was a mild evening. On board the trailer were various vessels containing an assortment of liquids and blackening materials. Three buckets of joe, a bag of mash, treacle, spent oil, flour and sawdust. The fun was about to begin.

Out of Glen Duffer's gate, banging bits of two by twos on the boggy's side, blowing on two home made trumpets made from copper piping and rubber hose. Up the hill to Balvenie Street towards the heart of Pagoda City, and a drink in each hostelry. The least black of the blackening crew would enter the pub with the kitty and drinks order, while outside a sing-song erupted, and carried well down the street in the otherwise still evening air. Onto the next pub, and the next, until they return to their local for a good hose down round the back, and a well earned dram for the tractor driver.

By the time wives and girlfriends arrived to enjoy the fun, some blackners were well on their way to oblivion. It has been known for future brides and grooms on their blackening night to be tied to the pole of a street light for several hours for the entertainment of passers by, and to endure some self-embarrassment. Fortunately Willie was spared that humiliation.

7

Saturday the third of July was hen and stag night. Another round of the Dufftown pubs (that's twice round as there's only four pubs) starting with a basket supper in the Fife. Basket suppers were fried chicken and chips served in a woven basket, and were all the rage in lounge bars in the early to mid seventies, but in Dufftown in nineteen seventy nine, basket suppers were still in vogue.

Pam's hen night started in Aberlour, and having done the rounds there, the well-oiled group of friends hired a minibus to take them to down town Dufftown. Stag and hen nights the world over are all about the consumption of booze, drinking as much as you can, and staying on your feet for as long as possible. The definition of a good stagger is: 'people who's brains have deserted their feet, and whose faces tell us they've gone to another world'.

8

July the seventeenth dawned on Speyside, and up out of bed bouncing on top form was a wired Willie. This was his day.

'I'm doing this once, and once only,' Willie thought to himself. 'I'm going to enjoy myself, it's my wedding, wi' all my mates in the one place at the same time. How often in my life will that happen?'

In the Grant camp there was a buzz, Sharny dubs was all spruced up like a ferm hoose for sale. Pam's dad had taken the byre brush to the close, and raked a' the chukies at the front door. Two days earlier he'd trimmed the hedge, mowed the lawn, an' did the edgin'. Family members were home from Canada for the wedding, and the sprucing up was as much for their benefit as Pam's.

Home baking day in the Sharny Dubs' kitchen usually fell on a Tuesday, but with the extra people at the table each night Mrs Grant was up early Thursday morning baking extra scones, pancakes, oatcakes, and queen cakes all before the weary travellers came downstairs for breakfast. Friday evening's service rehearsal at the parish church went smoothly with everyone falling into line with the minister's protocol for the real thing next day.

Having spent her last few hours as a single woman in the hairdresser's and beautician's chairs, Pam emerged with a dottled bum which could only be put right with a glass of her dad's cheap bubbly. Pam was relaxed and radiant, and looking a million dollars as she and her dad waited on her bride's car to take them to Aberlour. Local Dufftown photographer Johnny Carricker was photographing Pam's bridesmaids, and her mother at the church door as she stepped gingerly from the vintage Austin Seven, displaying her wedding dress and finery to the collective crowd that always gathers when the whisper of a village wedding is taking place.

Willie and his best man Ronnie were already at the alter having had their pep talk with the minister in the vestry.

"There are many good reasons to get married, Willie."

"You can get your tax back," put in Willie.

"Yes, and two can live as cheap as one!"

"And there's always someone else to get up and change the channel on t.v!"

9

Two thirty rang on the church clock as the beadle opened the doors for the newly married Mr and Mrs Thompson to step out, and face the crowd of onlookers (where they go during the service is a mystery in every town).

The Spey valley was basking under a blue cloudless sky, and photographer Johnny, a master with fill in flash, was confident that in some if not most of the wedding pictures, people's eyes would be open. The Austin Seven chugged its way to Dufftown's Memorial Hall where the feast and the fun would be held.

Once the dreaded speeches were done with, the tables cleared, the woman powdering their noses, the men at the bar all saying, "what a great meal it was", "the best part of any wedding day could begin".

Drams flew from the gantry optics to all corners of the temporary bar constructed in the left corner of the hall. The ceilidh band were making ready to start the evening's dance with the grand march, the half dozen children of invited guests were having great fun sliding up and down the hall floor on the freshly sprinkled dance dust. Aunties were chatting feverishly about a family relative who was unable to attend the wedding due to a resent spell in hospital.

"Aye, but we'll ging in by her the morn wi' a bitty cake."

"Fit aboot a' your folk, are they a' fine?"

"Well, Mary's nae that great iv noo. She hisnae been

herself lately, bit she's got the doctor again next week, maybe they'll get tae the bottom o' it this time."

"She got peels fae him last month, but they dinna seem tae hiv deen ony good."

"Aye, its nae fine fan foulkes nae weel."

As the four bar strains of an accordion began to drown out the chitter chatter, Willie was dragged from his mates at the bar to take his position on the dance floor to start the grand march with his bride, Pam. Within seconds ten couples, then twenty, were in battle formation down the hall flanks, sweeping any unsuspecting bystander into their forward path.

10

During the next five hours, all aspects of human nature would be displayed in one form or another. Emotions and senses would all surface and spill over, new romances would begin, old romances may end, and adolescents encounter their first taste of alcohol, their first drag o' a fag, and perhaps on the way home their first sexual experience.

Dance dram, dance dram, dance dram, Scottish weddings find their own rhythm. The more the drams flow, the more the evening swings. Tea, sandwiches and sausage rolls arrive from the hall kitchen around nine, and Willie's buddies from the pipe band give an impromptu concert forming a circle in the middle of the dance floor. Barely able to stand, some pipers are so musically inept they can get as drunk as skunks and still hold a tune without dropping a note or falling over.

Pacing himself well in the dram stakes, Willie was working his way round the Thompson clan while they were still reasonably sober. After a couple of sandwiches and a sausage roll, he was planning to penetrate the ranks of Pam's relations, and dazzle them with his couthie conversation until the eleven o'clock mark, after which time all inhibitions are conquered and that other person inherits their body.

Some of the more distant Grant relatives who didn't even know before the wedding who Pamela was marrying, warmed quickly to Willie's charms.

"He seems a fine loon"; "Pamela's got herself a nice lad there"; "An' they've biggit a fine hoose tee"; "aye, they'll dee aright."

The bewitching hour of midnight was approaching, and some of the revellers looked the worse for wear, with kilts at half mast, sporrans slung low on hips like they were Scottish cowboys, socks round ankles, white shirts open to the waist, collars up at one side. Thank God they were mostly hired kilts fae Chishoms in Commerce Street, Elgin, and would be well inspected before their return to the shop on Monday morning.

Auld lang syne resounded, raising the Dufftownites' nationalistic instincts just about high enough to follow on with, 'He's a jolly good fellow', not knowing or even caring that it was an English song. English or not it fits the place it has been given to complete the traditional Scottish wedding.

And as the band's MC, on behalf of his band, bids goodnight to the dance, and drink weary roustabouts, a new chapter in Willie's life begins.

11

The first and most memorable night of his honeymoon,

even though they were Italy bound, was spent in the elegance of the honeymoon suite in the Rothes Glen Hotel. To have breakfast in the same dinning room as racing driver legend Jackie Stewart, while being on honeymoon, Willie just thought he was in seventh heaven, until Pam reminded him they had a five hour drive ahead to catch the tea time flight to Milan.

"Pam, it's a Mini Cooper S we're goin' in, nae a Hillman *Limp*! We'll be there by four, no worries."

"Cut the Aussie lingo Willie, it's Italy we're goin to, nae Oz!"

"Oh bella bella," began Willie.

"Bella bella, yersel! Jist drive."

12

Their first two days in Italy, they explored Milan before moving to the shores of Lake Garda, and Bardolino, a pleasant shore side town with its abundant share of Italian hospitality. Waiters with impeccable manners, like it was effortless, and second nature to be serving their customers.

"If we had service like this at home, Pam, we'd go out more often. Remember that steak supper in Elgin when the waitress threw our plates on the table sayin' 'we've nae onion rings left, we've gein ye carrots instead, an' if you'd come in earlier the chips wid have been warmer'?"

"Yeah, what a horror meal that was. I'm sure she wis getting' drunker wi' every course she slammed on the table."

"We may only be your average Dufftown couple, but we're worth better than that. It's really only when you come abroad you realise how bad the service is at home. The

Scots have a long way to go in learning tourist skills, every where else you go in the world, the service industry people can't do enough for you."

"We've got such fabulous scenery in Scotland, as spectacular as anywhere, but we're just so rude to our visitors." added Pam.

The orange sunset over Lake Garda was a picture postcard scene, with moored pleasure craft silhouetted and bobbing gently offshore as Pam and Willie sipped their cappuccinos, recalling uncle Gordon's favourite saying: "What are the poor people doing now?'

13

Next morning saw them on the road to Venice (at what point does the road to Venice stop, and the canals start?), with it gondolas and glass, canals and motor launches.

"Venicans must get an awful lot of haircuts, Pam, look at all them barbers poles! Instead of Barry Gahooly you'll get Giovanni di Conti's version of short back an sides."

"Gee, aren't the Italians just so good looking, and such classy dressers, they must be in the top five best looking people in the world, way better looking than Americans, Canadians, Aussies, Germans, French, British or Chinese."

"They might be very good looking, but they dinna' know where to build cities! This one's sinking, look at a' they pigeons wi' webbed feet."

The honeymooners were loving Italy, but their days of pasta an' spamanti were soon to give way to piece denners, and flasks o' coffee back at work. Many people visiting Italy, leave feeling they have made a spiritual connection. People who are travellers (those who can live happily anywhere in the world) will always tell you, Italy is something special. Home birds too know what is meant by the saying, 'see Naples and die'.

14

Summer was giving way to autumn in Speyside, when Willie's father was offered a retirement package by the company, a generous lump sum, and an adequate pension. Having given nearly forty years to distilling whisky he had no hesitation in accepting the company's offer. During a couple of weeks holiday he was due, the management sorted out their staff promotions, and as of November the first that year, Willie was on the managerial trail in the position of assistant brewer.

As assistant brewer, Willie had responsibilities covering all the processes engaged in getting the whisky from the barley to the barrel. Checking and double-checking all the departments' recordings to ensure the alcohol going into the warehouses was prime quality.

"If it's good stuff going in, it'll be great stuff coming out," he would say as he made his daily checks.

Willie was fitting in well in his new roll as assistant brewer, and for the following twelve months kept his head down, listening and learning. The extra wages that came with the promotion were very welcome at home as Pam was about to start maternity leave from the bank. In eight weeks, Willie and Pam's life would change forever with the birth of their first child. No one before the event seems to quite explain how suddenly different your life becomes when that tiny person emerges into the world. As soon as he or she comes home everything you do from that moment on is for them. Grandparents may often hand on their advice, but nine times out of ten it falls short of the mark.

15

While draming the boys with their five pm Friday broonic, Willie was called away to the Stephen Memorial Hospital as Pam was at a crucial stage of labour, and within a couple of hours their son, Gary, was born. Blue eyed, blonde haired, and with distinctive features, the Thompson blood line looked safe.

"We can only hope he'll grow out of it," said Pam smiling and smug, "In time he'll look like a Speyside Grant."

Baby Gary arrived home to the family's Cabrach nest a few days later, to grow up like his dad in the timeless territory. With his promotion to assistant brewer, and a new family member to spend time with, Willie's commitment to playing his bagpipes and making himself available for the pipe band was waning. Instead of highland games and village fetes it was picnics and long walks in the countryside pushing baby Gary's pram, sometimes along the Cabrach roads, sometimes along the banks of the Spey. Sundays were usually spent at Sharny Dubs farm, as it was Pam's parents' first grandchild they were keen to see their grandson as much as possible.

16

Long summer Cabrach evenings caressed the souls of the country folk, while town dwellers chilled out with a long cool beer in their local. Country people strolled through their vegetable gardens with a mug of coffee, kicking out any protruding weeds that dared show themselves. Although Willie's garden wasn't established, he did have a healthy showing of early tatties, which he'd planted to break in the virgin ground. Next year, if Willie's plans materialised, his dad will be in charge of knocking the garden into shape, while Willie concentrated more on landscaping issues.

Willie and Pam had now been nearly two years in their Cabrach Castle enjoying their captivating view, and the comforting warmth of their wood burner when the weather turned. Starting a family right away after getting married maybe wasn't their plan, but when the mercury's high, love and lust are a formidable combination to keep at bay, and the Cabrach television reception wasn't that good.

Summer nineteen seventy-six was particularly hot with the North East of Scotland experiencing temperatures more akin to the Mediterranean. It wasn't just the heat that was so memorable, but the fact it went on for weeks on end, something that in the north east was rare and only happens once in a life time.

He was too young to know, but for ten week old Gary Thompson this was the warmest he was ever going to be in the Cabrach. Throughout Speyside, still men and mash men were known to only be wearing dungarees during the heat wave, mash rooms and still houses generally hover around eighty degrees Fahrenheit, but during the seventy six roasting they were an unbearable one hundred degrees. Every shift was like working in a virtual sauna for eight hours which kept still and mash man's bodies well detoxed and trim.

Despite such a fabulous summer, many poor folk had already booked their holidays to Spain and further afield just to get the sun - but if the sun was the main reason for their holiday you'd think they'd go and live in Australia or similar sun soaked garden of Eden. In the summer of seventy-six there was nowhere else in the world a better place to be than Northeast Scotland. With such a fantastic summer you would've thought the barley harvest might be a month early, but apparently it doesn't work like that. You may get twice the amount of sunshine, but twice the sunshine probably means half the rain, and crops won't grow without equal amounts, so the Cabrach harvest in seventy six was only about a week earlier, good enough, though, to get the bales in before the first snow fall of the Cabrach winter.

A pal of Willie's arrived for a beer. "Noo that you're assistant brewer, Willie, div ye miss yer days in the warehouse, sookin' up the whisky intae yer dog? Div ye ken that in years to come, some o' that stuff that wis pinched will be sellin' for hunners if nae thousands o' pounds? There will be rare malt collectors that wid ge their best drinking erm for a taste o' the stuff you've drunk!"

"Possibly," said Willie, "I particularly remember one butt in warehouse three, stuff that was made in nineteen thirty-three. Jock, Davy an myself were dein' the sampling, and the taste o' the stuff in that butt wis jist heavenly. But dozens o' warehousemen all over Scotland have tasted the cratur at it's purest and best. We live wi' the stuff, and I suppose to us its just whisky, and dinna appreciate it haein' any other value than that o' drinkin' it."

"Just watch," said the visitor, "as the years roll on, distilleries will find new ways of generating income."

"Well, if that's nae as good a hint as I've heard, fit are ye for? A Glen Auchtie, a Glen Kinvie, a Ben Conval, or een oot o' my barrel?"

"Need ye ask, Willie? We'll start wi' the barrel."

Willie's barrel, made for him by a cooper friend, sat on his living room dresser, the centerpiece of his drinks display. It had been sherried, and held about a gallon of the purest, mildest whisky ever distilled, deep brown in colour with a bead that stuck to the inside of the glass (similar to a good pint of Guinness), and was mellow, oaky with a smooth chocolatey aftertaste. The kind of dram that entices you to want another, and as Willie got up to replenish their glasses, there was a knock at his back door.

"Come in," shouts Willie from the top of his lounge stairs. "Och, it's Ronnie an' Joe. You're just in time for a dram, boys. I'll get mair ice."

The friends clinked their glasses, chunky cut crystal, toasting their good fortune in friendship. One good dram leads to two good drams and two good drams lead to six better drams, and soon it's double figures, and double vision.

"Just one more for the ditch," insists Willie. "There must be one left in the barrel yet - we'll teem 'er afore morning, but dawn was minutes away from winning the race, as fast as night time passed for the four friends, a new day was upon them, and even the best of drinking friends have to give way to the inconvenience of sleep. Jim and Ronnie were shown to a bedroom with a quadruple bed (that's a double double, it was all they could see after their all night session). Joe snored his head off on the couch for four hours in unconsciousness then Pam did her dutiful deed running the boys home to Dufftown and Aberlour to further sleep off their nights over indulgence.

CHAPTER NINE

MANAGEMENT

1

Willie's destiny seemed like it was a chronologically written map especially written for his life. Right from the day in class at age fourteen when the careers officer visited the school to ascertain the ambitions of that term's school leavers.

Working his way along the row of pupils with his question, 'What's your name, and what do you want to do when you leave school?', he was offering advice to the regular answers of nurse, teacher, joiner, electrician, secretary, plumber. But Willie's answer to his tedious question left him startled, and speechless for a moment, while he tried to work out Willie's reply.

"You want to be a distillery manager?"

"No," said Willie, "I'm GOING to be a distillery manager!"

"Don't you have to get a job at a distillery first, Willie?"

'Well, that's obvious', thought Willie, but said nothing more, and the slightly shaken careers officer moved along the row of pupils hurrying through the last of the class.

At the distillery, Willie was on the verge of management, he just needed one more retirement, or onward move by the second in command, and he would move up a couple of notches to Assistant Manager. Glen Dufftown's manager, although a sprightly fifty eight year old, had nearly two years to go to retirement, but he had not been enjoying good health of late. Too much enjoying his managerial clout over a fruitful fifteen years was taking its toll on his flushing system, straining the organs that sustain life. But no matter how ill they are, old distillery managers can be thrawing, dogmatic creatures not willing to leave the job until their official retirement date, even when the concerns of Speyside doctors were aired in the distilling press they couldn't or wouldn't give up the habit of a life time.

Giving up their post, many managers may have thought, wouldmean giving up their personal supply of the 'cratur', but surely there would be ways and means of ensuring that such a thing didn't happen. If sensibility was to prevail, the manager's post would become vacant by the end of the month, although the gearing up of staff into new positions would probably take a few weeks of planning before everything fell into place.

2

September 1977, and Glen Dufftown distillery was about to resume production after the close season's maintenance shutdown. Willie was called into the manager's office for a meeting with the 'high heed yins', the production director, the company's general manager, and company secretary.

"Willie," says the general manager. "We want to get a feel from you how much you're enjoying your job. As far as we're concerned, everything seems to be running smoothly, your workload is always done ahead of schedule, and the extra two mashes a week you've coped with no problems at all. We're happy with you. Are you happy with us?"

"My job is my lifeblood," replied Willie. "I've wanted to be in distilling since I was at school. It's the only career I ever considered."

"Following in your dad's footsteps - and your grandfather's, of course," spouted the production director, smiling coyly at Willie. "Well, we'd like to offer you the manager's job with effect from now should you want it." said a hopeful general manager.

Beaming from ear to ear Willie had no hesitation in accepting the promotion, and thanked his senior employers with passion, shaking their hands vigorously. The rest of the day he couldn't help repeating to himself, "I'm the manager... I'm the manager... I'm the manager of Glen Dufftown...", and couldn't wait for five o'clock to come so he could hurry home to tell Pam.

Five pm eventually came, and as he zoomed down Conval Street in his hurry to get home, he misjudged the Cabrach turn off. Swerving to avoid a collision with an oncoming vehicle, his car mounted the verge and rolled down the bank into the Dullan water ending up on its roof.

Although the Dullan at that spot is quite shallow, Willie could have easily drowned if knocked unconscious by the impact. But luck and perhaps fate were in control of the incident, and Willie escaped with only a few cuts and bruises. His car was extensively damaged, and by the time he eventually got home all the excitement of his promotion was very secondary to that day's events. For the remainder of the week, Pam drove Willie to work, and in Saturday's Northern Scot Willie found a replacement for his beloved Mini Cooper S.

3

Two weeks into Willie's managerial role, a crisis hit the night shift operators while taking over their duties from the back shift boys.

"How's your wash doin', is it due o'er?" was the usual cry in the tun room as the mash men changed shifts. A similar change was also taking place in the still house, the coming on shift still man needed to know if it was the low wines bubbling in the copper still or if it was the second charge. A glance at the record book would of course answer the question, but having changed over on shifts with the same guy year after year his word was gospel. It would be well into the night before a still man would normally be making his entry notes, and if any function had been overlooked, a situation could arise that was not retrievable.

The still house clock ticked past four am, too early to get up, too late to go to bed, and the normally smooth running routine for the mash man and still man was to be launched into chaos. Excess pressure in the copper wash still blew the seals in the feed and draining pipes causing production to shut down until a morning inspection could take place.

Newly appointed rookie manager Willie Thompson was called at five thirty am to be on site at the 6 am shift change over, and full briefing on what had taken place.

After digesting all the facts from the shift operators, and the brewer, he had no hesitation in handing out his punishment, and fired both mash man and still man.

Defending his decision when asked to reconsider his sacking of the men, he simply said: "Their failure to carry out their responsibilities has cost the company many thousands of pounds, and is threfore a sackable offence. Get on with the paperwork. I'm going home to have breakfast."

"I'm sorry, boys," said the brewer, offering his sympathies. "Maybe if he hadnae been sae new tae the job..."

"Who would've thought oor Willie wid be as nesty as that? It jist shows ye, gie a man power, and he trades his soul."

In the course of one incident, Willie had gone from good guy to villain, a course from which he could never backtrack.

"Arrogance beyond belief," thought the brewer. "I'll hae tae watch my step. Any slip up an I'll be doon the road ana. My god, I've niver seen sic a change in a' person. One day he's your work mate, next day a right bastard. I hope for the sake o' a decent working atmosphere he's nae gonna continue wi' his heavy handed tactics, maybe the still wis bein run a little easy oozy at times, but we're only makin' whisky nae carryin' oot brain surgery."

The men took their sacking hard. Not for the carelessness they displayed in their duties, but the fact they were fired by a manager so much their junior. The audacity of such a young upstart showing them no mercy severely dented their pride. Willie had showed his ruthlessness when pricing materials for building his house, but this was way beyond trying to get the best price, this was a power surge to demonstrate his position, a clear message to say that he wasn't one of the boys anymore, he was distillery manager Willie Thompson, come of age at thirty five, and he wasn't going to stop there.

By late afternoon, the engineers had fixed the faults, and production had resumed. The breakdown had lost the distillery two mashes and two distillations, and with the parts and the engineer's time to pay for, it equated to quite a hefty bill.

4

With the sacking of the mash man and still man, a reshuffling of the staff ensued, creating a vacancy within the warehouse squad. So within two weeks of becoming manager, Willie had fired and hired, crashed his car, and made enemies at the still - a pretty eventful fortnight he told Pam as he poured a stress-busting dram from his drinks display barrel.

"Maybe you were a bit hasty sacking the men, Willie, showing your bad side too soon."

"Well, I just felt I needed to stamp my authority right where it would hurt. They knew they'd made a big blunder, and I couldn't let it go. Two weeks into becoming manager I had to show who was boss. Had it been a year down the road, I'd probably give them a bollocking, and that would be it."

Willie sipped his dram, but wasn't enjoying it as normal, Pam's comments were prying on his mind, then he recalled something his granddad said to him as a fifteen year old, "You'll surprise yourself, Willie, just how high you can fly if you participate in the water of life."

"Pam, I've grown up fast in two weeks, I've had to

show the other side of my character - you might say, Pam, it's my bad side. Harsh as I was, it was necessary for my career and our survival. I'm the boss now, and the high heed yins are watching me!"

Willie was convincing himself as distillery manager his decisions were right, Pam was concerned his arrogance would spill over into family life, but right now he needed her support, and she slipped onto the large comfy sofa, nestling herself into Willie's space with a reassuring cuddle.

5

Pleasant autumn days were giving way to frosty winter nights when Pam had some good news for Willie on his return from work. Her visit to the doctor confirmed what she had suspected - she was pregnant.

"Fantastic, that's brilliant Pam." Willie was ecstatic/ "Even wi' the stress's and strains o' management, the old boy's still working. Let's hope it's a girl, no a boy for Gary to play with... oh no, it could be twins!"

"Calm doon, Willie. There's only one, but the doctor couldn't tell which species."

Willie sighed. "God, it's great. How old's Gary?"

"He's eighteen months, his birthday's in April."

That's right, the tenth."

"No, Willie, the fifteenth - ten days before the twenty fifth."

"I knew ten had something to do with it! We better hae a celebration dram. Oh, no, you canna, Pam."

"I'll just have a small sherry, Willie, just this once."

And they toasted the baby, cuddling up close on their lounge sofa.

"Have you told Gary?", Willie asked.

"No, I thought we'd wait a while till the baby starts to show, then he might understand better, but we can tell him now if you like."

"Yeah, give him a shout."

"Gary, Gary, we're in the living room!"

With a scuttle of feet, wee Gary raced from playing with his toys on the kitchen carpet to his dad's outstretched arms. "Mummy wants to tell you something nice."

"Gary, daddy and mummy are going to have a new baby for you to play with. Isn't that great? You'll have a sister or a brother, and you'll have lots of fun together."

At eighteen months old, Gary had no idea what they were talking about, but smiled and laughed anyway, he was just happy to have been summoned for the consultation.

Gary was the usual wee mischievous boy, soon to start 'the terrible twos' syndrome. All parents know that rebellious affliction, which doesn't pass until they're four, but to his mum and dad he was totally adorable, with his shock of thick blonde shiny hair that almost covered his sparkling clear bright blue eyes.

"In seven months or so, Gary, you're gonna have a wee sister or brother. But now it's time for your bath and off to bed." But in a flash Gary somehow managed to escape his dad's clutches, and raced off to hide. But his bid for freedom was short lived, and the evening routine of getting him ready for bed got underway. While dad ran the bath, mum got fresh clothes for Gary in the morning, undressed him, then dad bathed and dried him. Mum then dressed him in his jim jams, tucked him into bed with a five minute story, and dad poured another well deserved dram - for himself, not Gary.

6

Although whisky was first distilled in Scotland three or four centuries ago, it was not until the 1800s before it was bestowed to other parts of the world. Whisky may not be the oldest spirit ever distilled, but it has a uniqueness in its colour and a taste all its own. It is to be enjoyed, and, above all, respected.

Many good men and woman down through history have succumb to its charms thinking they were whisky's master. So called malt whisky experts for many years have been writing about its virtues, but it's the whisky itself that has the last word. Speyside is home to more than half Scotlands malt distilleries, and with ten million barrels collectively maturing in their warehouses at one time, that's a hell of lot o' whisky for each Speyside whisky drinker, minus of course the two percent angels share.

"If only I'd worked that one out for myself," said Willie reading from the 'enchanter' monthly whisky mag. "I would've thought the 'enchanter' magazine would have been about bagpipes nae whisky," he said to Pam.

"Well, whisky and bagpipes go together, so there will be a connection," replied Pam missing the pun completely, she was too preoccupied with tidying up Gary's clothes and toys from the living room floor.

Willie poured himself another dram, and a sherry for Pam when she was finally ready to sit and relax after tucking Gary into bed.

"That's three you've had," said Pam, accusing Willie of pouring extra big ones, "and it's nae eight o' clock yet."

"But, Pam, I'm only relieving a little tension from the day's stresses an' strains. It's nae easy bein' manager. The job's a bit mair demandin' than pressing buttons in the still hoose. I've tae hae lunch wi' the boss o' the copperies, and play golf two afternoons a week, it's all stressful stuff."

"Lunches, golf, then you come hame tae drams, I canna see the stress in that."

"Och, Pam, I'm only havin' fun. I'm the manager, and it's a breeze, just enjoy the ride." The whisky was starting to talk, Willie was getting too carefree, but bit his tongue just in time before saying too much.

7

Having worked for a few years on shifts at Glen Dufftown, Willie was used to getting up to start work at six in the morning, although as manager his starting time was nine o'clock he'd usually be on the go most mornings by six, eager to get on with his day's tasks. Some days he'd cut the grass at the front of the house (a job he hated), do a little paperwork or wash his car before anyone else in the household stirred.

The family's new arrival was still a few weeks away, but excitement in the household was building. Pam, like all expectant mothers, was over prepared for the birth with cotton wool up to her eyeballs, fresh towels, and hundreds of nappies neatly stacked in the spare bedroom. Everything that a baby would ever need, including the kitchen sink, was in the spare bedroom - although in this scenario the 'kitchen sink' was an oval plastic blue baby bath. In fact, there were *two* plastic baths, one blue, one pink."You can't bathe a baby girl in a blue bath, it's bad luck Willie," insisted Pam. Willie felt she was taking the micky, and coyly smiled like an obedient expectant husband should.

The week before the birth date seemed like a month.

"When those waters break, Pam, we're gonna have to get the fire brigade up here to pump out the flooded parks into the Fiddoch, the whole valley doon past Auchindoon will be on flood alert."

"Well, that'll be the least of my worries, Willie. I'll be on my back, groanin', puffin', shovin', and doped up past the eye balls wi' laughin' gas, showin' a' my bits to the maternal world."

"Well, I hope I can get doon the road past the engines to the hospital. They'll probably hae tae call oot the Aiberlour and Rothes boys ana."

Although Willie hadn't taken official holidays with the birth imminent, he'd relinquished his 'on call' duties for two weeks. Then in the middle of the second week, as he was dozing off in his armchair at midnight, a call from the maternity ward came through.

"Mr Thompson, I think you should come in now, things are beginning to happen," said a calm and collected mid wifery voice. A copy of 'Fishing and Shooting' slid off his knee as he stood up and grabbed his car keys from the side table. Willie sped down to the Dufftown hospital in record time with a good hour or so to spare before his and Pam's daughter Amy Louise Thompson made her appearance, weighing in at a healthy seven and a half pounds, and displaying a good head of spiky blonde hair.

"Isn't she just gorgeous? You can easy tell I'm her dad," boasted a proud Willie, "And she's got blue eyes like you, Pam."

"All babies have blue eyes Willie, do you not remember when Gary was born?"

"Oh yeah, I forgot about that."

"She might have the Thompson colour, but she's definitely got the Grant nose and ears," said an insistent Pam.

"Is that a nose for whisky and an ear for music?" retorted Willie, tongue in check.

"Willie behave. Are you nae wanting to go home and get some sleep?" Willie kissed Pam and his new daughter, thanked the maternity staff, and headed up the Cabrach road with a huge grin on his face to get a few hours' well deserved sleep.

8

By mid morning Willie was up, out of bed and on the phone to each set of parents expressing his joy on his and Pam's new arrival, and to his pals, whom he knew were up for a drink at their local.

Grabbing the family camera, Willie headed down to Dufftown for a midday wetting of the baby's head, and with a feeling of freedom as he entered his local to meet his pals. For the next few hours he was a man alone without husbandry and parenting responsibilities: son Gary was with Pam's parents at their farm, Pam and baby Amy were safe at the hospital, Willie could party with his mates and drink himself into a stupor if he so wished.

Three or four drams were very soon accompanying his pint on the bar as word of the new baby girl reached the ears of the regulars, but before getting too messed up Willie wanted to get down to the hospital to take a few photos.

"Give me an hour, guys. I've got to get the shots, then we can dram all day." And so Willie staggered and ran, ran and staggered, his way to the hospital where he captured Pam and baby for the family album in such a competent way that Pam guessed he only had had a couple of drams.

"I'm only meeting Ronnie and Jim at the Fife, I winna be too late home. I'll need to go in tomorrow to check on a few things at the still, then I'll come in by the hospital at teatime."

"Isn't she just beautiful, Pam? We're so lucky having a boy and a girl. It's pretty special, really. We're very, very lucky."

Willie took another couple of shots of his girls, and headed off, pleased as punch to meet up with his mates in the Fife for a wetting of the baby's head to top any wetting that had gone before.

9

Whisky spirit is big business whether you are making it or drinking it, and nowhere is that more relevant than for the people of Speyside - and some Speysiders can be more serious about drinking it than those who make it.

The serious connoisseurs know their Glens, Glenlivet, Glenfiddoch, Glenfarclas, Glen Grant, Glenmorangie, Glen Keith, Glentauchers, Glen Rothes, Glen Alachie, Glen Elgin, but Willie's favourite malt was Glen Dufftown, the whisky he grew up with, and was now in charge of making sure its continued production would remain at the highest standard possible.

Willie, Ronnie and Jim got toot a roo, visiting all of Dufftown's watering holes at least once in their six or seven hour drinking spree before crashing out at Jim's Conval Street abode. A sobering ten-minute walk next morning saw Willie getting to Glen Dufftown a few minutes after nine to attend to his managerial duties. Once he'd done his daily checks, made some phone calls, and had his routine briefing by the brewer, he could disappear off home to nurse his hangover until making a visit around teatime to see Pam and Amy.

Willie had two more evenings of blissful solitude before his peace and quiet would be shattered, and the house ring with family sounds again. He called Pam's mum to speak to Gary

"Are you doin' fine son? Good. I'll pick you up, and we'll go to the hospital to see mum and your new sister, how's that?"

"Great dad, what time are you coming?"

"I'll pick you up in half an hour, okay? Put Granny Margaret back on. Margaret, are you coming to see your daughter and grand daughter? Okay. I'll be round in half an hour."

"We'll see you then Willie," said an excited Margaret about seeing her first grand daughter.

Willie again took his camera to the hospital to capture some early shots of Gary holding Amy, and of course granny was on hand to take a Thompson family group. Willie had just recently got into photography; he was keen on the golf but felt he needed some other pastime, and photography seemed to fit the bill.

After a couple of visits to Coates Photographic Supplies in Elgin, he treated himself to the best amateur photographer's gear available. Like when Willie took up golf after his footballing days, a couple of irons and a club weren't good enough to start with, he had to go the whole hog and buy top of the range golf clubs in the latest trolley bag. Now, whether Les Coates was making the biggest margin, or he genuinely thought for Willie's needs, the very recently released Olympus OM1 was the camera Willie should have, Willie would never know for sure. With lenses, including standard, wide angle, telephoto and a compact flashgun, all packed into a tidy shoulder camera bag, Willie was equipped for any photographic assignment.

His first couple of films through the camera were showing his inexperience in using a single lens reflex 35mm camera, but by the time he'd shot his fifth film he was proving to be very competent. He was a natural on the football field, and on the golf course, and more than holding his own at taking photographs.

10

Over the following weekend, as there was no rush for Pam's bed, the hospital staff decided to keep her and Amy from going home as a matter of routine, much to the annoyance of Pam and the exuberance of Willie. He just couldn't believe his luck. Pam and Amy were in perfect health with no after birth effects between them, and he was getting another three nights' grace! Gary was delighted to be staying at his granny's, with lots of freedom, an endless choice of toys, plus the thrill of accompanying his granddad on the tractor during the day, so for him it was an extended holiday.

Willie immediately planned his weekend with a round of golf on Saturday morning at Moray golf club in Lossiemouth with the brewer and manager from Glen Moray Distillery, Elgin. To play some golf away from the hills of Dufftown must be a welcoming treat, even for the biggest diehard Dufftonairian golfer who plays their golf on the unique three in one course - even to climb to the fifth tee a participant needs crampons, oxygen, and a flag of their country.

Willie's weekend flew, and Monday arrived very quick and very welcome - he'd had enough free time, and was more than ready for his family life to resume at home. The time apart Willie exploited well, but was more than glad to have them all back under one roof (his roof!) and get on with family life, concentrating on their future.

Back at work, the distillery staff were full of congratulations for Willie and Pam, even to the extent of suggesting Willie should name a special filling after his new daughter - and so was born the manager's dram. An idea so simple but so very effective as it gave Glen Dufftown another malt to add to their growing choice of whiskies. Presentation and packaging is the name of the game, Willie kept on telling his key employees.

"It's a'right makin' a' this whisky, but we have got to sell it or we're oot o' a job. We ken we mak' the best whisky on Speyside, but we have to package and market it right."

Willie's input into the packaging became more evident with each launch of a new label design. Muted atmospheric colours with a sepia toned image replaced a straight forward wordy label, making the bottle more attractive and eye catching on the shelf of the off licence. Willie's artistic eye as a photographer led him to doodle draw while in his manager's office. He would draft a few ideas and send them off to the design house in Glasgow, and the final result would never be far from Willie's original sketch.

Another close season was imminent, slightly later by a few weeks than the previous year, but just at the right time for the Thompson family, and Willie took full advantage of his two weeks off by collaring his father to help him crack on with marking out the vegetable garden, fence erecting, and spread the five ton of chuckies for the front of the house that had been delivered three months earlier.

What seemed at first to be quiet a big job, the spreading and leveling only took Willie and his dad three hours, and so pleased were they with their efforts they celebrated by having a relaxing dram and can of beer.

Willie's Cabrach castle, from the front at least, was looking grander, and with his dad's help the landscaping at the back and sides of the house would not take a lifetime.

Pam was conjuring with many household chores as baby Amy slept off her morning feed in her pram at the back door. Gary, in the meantime, was engaged in some serious earth removing operation with his giant yellow digger, tractor and trailer, and for extra buoyancy he would shovel some earth down his wellie boots, running into his mum making noises and pointing to his feet.

By mid afternoon, the men folk had erected a wooden fence along the boundary to the property where grass seed would be sown, providing a safe play area for the children. Late afternoon, Willie's mum was due to arrive on the scene to join the family for tea. Pam was cooking up one of her special road kill stews with new tatties fae her mum and dad's garden. Unlike fresh hot butteries, new tatties are one food you can never tire of: you can boil them, fry them, chip them, roast them, bake them, and finally eat them, and never feel more satisfied.

So at thirty-three Willie Thompson had reached a stage in life where the achievable dreams of a Dufftown schoolboy had come to fruition. Happily married with a son and a daughter, owner of his own house, and manager at Glen Dufftown Distillery. 'How far can I go with promotion?', he pondered as he gazed out his office window across the yard to the granite stoned still house. 'I've flown this far on whisky wings, how high can I soar?'

Willie's mind was buzzing with all sorts of thoughts about his future career prospects. 'I could just do my job as manager until I retire, and that would be cool. Or if I really wanted to be ambitious, I could try for a company directorship'.

He was all fired up, but needed to air his thoughts with Pam to bring his thinking back onto a more level plain. So after bathing Gary, and tucking him into bed (Amy was already asleep), and telling him to keep quiet or he'd wake his little sister, Willie set up two good house drams for himself and Pam. Pam enjoyed a whisky but preferred a dash of lemonade in it rather than ice or water.

"What do you think, Pam?" asked Willie, handing over her dram.

"Think? About what?"

"Well, do you think I should try for more promotion, or just be content with being a manager?"

"Well, it's really up to you Willie. You've got a good salary as manager, do we need the extra money? And do you need the added stress?"

"A good point, Pam. The stress could be a big factor. It'd be great to be getting more money and have a bigger car, but the extra responsibility could bring its problems."

"Yeah - when you've got problems you just pour bigger drams."

"That's maybe so, Pam, but I've got it in check, the drink'll nae get a hud o' me."

"Well, I hope not Willie. But just lately there seems to be more empty bottles than usual. If you're gonna go for promotion, you'll have to slow it down."

"Okay, I'll just have the two tonight."

"I mean it, Willie. Some nights you're drinking too much, and on occasions you've come home wi' a shot in, I'm going to mark the bottles for the next two weeks, then we'll revalue the situation. Your responsibility to me and the kids is paramount. If promotion is gonna turn you into a raging alcoholic, then you better just stay a manager."

11

The writing was on the wall for Willie's drinking culture, his domestic family bliss would be in jeopardy if he didn't *nip* it in the bud. He knew using the occupational hazard line with Pam wouldn't cut the mustard, and made a conscious effort to keep his evening drams down to two, and by the third week he was only taking a dram every second night.

'Use it, don't abuse it', became Willie's favourite catchphrase for a while, especially when his in-laws visited. He was master of his job, master in his home, and now he was master over his drinking habits. The drinking slide is by far the easiest slope to slide on - you just keep drinking, and the tolerance keeps growing. You're still on your feet, but gradually you lose your mind, until one day you can't remember what day it is and you don't really care, as long as you get a drink. Then, once you've successfully drowned all your brain cells in alcohol, pickled your liver and ran out of money for extra strong mints, it's probably too late to fall off the slide, you're just as well to keep going until the big white light fades. Probably thanks mainly to Pam, Willie was a long way from even getting on to the slide, or the happy bus that only makes one stop - when it crashes. Alcohol is the most cunning of drugs, befriending you until you court it too much, then it betrays you big style, hanging on, not letting go, and promising you a good and better time with every sip. Alcohol is the good friend who can become the nightmare relation.

12

Over the following few years, Glen Dufftown's production of high quality spirit increased to a regular seven days, with only one shift being lost to cleaning. Gaining unrelenting respect from his brewer and staff, he was confident he could court promotion and still maintain the high standards at Glen Dufftown.

Willie likened life to being like playing golf. Keep practicing and your game improves, stop playing and your handicap soars. Willie played off seven, but in life he only knew pluses and was more than grateful for that, taking none of his successes for granted. He was clear in his mind on future promotion prospects, and wholeheartedly had the support of Pam, seeing no reason if promotion was on the horizon not to grasp it with both hands.

Family life in the Thompson's Cabrach Castle was idyllic, and with Gary now a well seasoned primary school pupil and Amy about to start her academic learning, there was space for Pam to be back in the job market. A few hours work each morning would earn her enough for a few of life's little extra luxuries (a holiday or Christmas fund was in the making). Having worked in the banking business

Pam nurtured a thrifty nature and kept a tight reign on the family purse strings, earning her the nickname, 'Pam the miser' from Willie. When a part time administrative job came up at Dufftown's Stephen Hospital offering flexible hours, it was right up Pam's street, and being the ideal candidate she strolled through the interview, starting the job the following Monday.

Although Willie's worth as manager at Glen Dufftown was invaluable to the company, should he wish to offer himself for future promotion, either within the company's structure or with another whisky maker, his bosses were understandably supportive. Willie was blessed with that 'Je ne sait quoi' (saying and doing the right thing at the right time), the art of wrapping people round his little finger, making them believe it's *them* who owe *him* a favour.

CHAPTER TEN

BRAND AMBASSADOR

1

In the summer of nineteen eighty-five, eight years after becoming manager, the company's brand ambassador was due to retire, and Willie fancied a crack at the post. Amy was well settled in at school, Gary had his friends, and Pam was happy in her part-time job, so there seemed to be no reason for Willie not to be jetting round the globe exuding the virtues of Glen Dufftown whisky.

Willie had the ideal credentials to be a brand ambassador, he was tall, handsome, and always smartly dressed, bordering on slickness. His easy manner made him comfortable in the company of the executive types, and could more than hold his own in conversation without being over dominant and too witty. He needed a new challenge and put his name forward for the job. Two weeks later he had an interview at the company's Glasgow headquarters, and by the body language signals coming from members of the board, Willie drove up the A9 confident he was the ambassador they wanted.

Sure enough, Willie's postman delivered the letter of

offer to his Cabrach castle only days later. A whole new career now beckoned. During his eight years as manager he'd overseen the making of millions of litres of Glen Dufftown malt whisky, now it was his job to sell it.

2

Willie's first overseas sales trip was to the biggest market place possible - America, The United States of. He needed to introduce himself to his company's agents in the big four across the pond, New York, Chicago, Los Angeles and San Francisco.

Twelve thousand miles in his first week was a helluva bit more than the fifty he normally clocked up between the Cabrach and Dufftown, yet he arrived home down after that, and the trips won't be so frequent, but it was exciting being in Dufftown on a Monday morning and L. A. on Wednesday night; it was some change to his working week.

Once Willie had done the rounds introducing himself to the companies agents in America and Europe he was keen to expand the sales of Glen Dufftown by opening up new markets in Australia, India, China and Indonesia. Willie had a global plan, of which the first part was to have Glen Dufftown being sold somewhere in each continent.

If anything, from the outside, Willie looked ambitious, but for him it was just an adventure in which he was playing the leading role. He'd he'd frequently say to himself, 'if it wasn't me, it would be someone else. I'm just here to enjoy the ride'.

Selling, to Willie, was just like a game: the more you sell, the more you want to sell, and the more you want to sell, the more exciting the game. He fully understood his worth to the company, but was also well aware that he was not irreplaceable. Willie could swing the lead more undetectable than most, his persona even without any higher education certificates or university degree shone bright and crystal clear.

When Willie's letter of offer had arrived, his first port of call was to Hepworth's men fitters in Elgin. He told Pam, "If I'm gonna be a success at selling Glen Dufftown, I'll need to look the part, so it's doon tae Hepworths for a made to measure."

Next stop was round the corner to Paterson's Shoe Shop to purchase a stylish pair of Oxford browns, then up Commerce Street to the ever reliable Johnny Rose's for a couple of shirts and ties. Successfully kited out within an hour without raking all over town, Willie grabbed a Lido coffee on the way back to his car, and was back home by lunchtime.

Hepworths had promised him his first fitting in two weeks, so to get him by on his first trip he bought a cheapy off the peg. If making whisky was an art so too was selling it, and to give himself half a chance Willie needed to look dapper, so investing in a made to measure suit was money well spent. If the outside looks good, it gives the inside a chance.

"I'm also gonna treat myself to a pair of Grenson full brogues after I sell my first hundred cases o' Glen Dufftown. Pam, I'm too excited - something's gonna give, life can't be this good without taking a fall somewhere down the line."

"Well I'm just happy to see you're happy, the new job could bring out the best in you, I suppose you were a bit fed up bein' at the still all day, you needed a change. You're excited because it's all brand new to you, and you want to do your best and sell, sell, sell."

"Pam, your psychology's good, I like it. Now, can you predict the 2.30 at Newmarket?"

"Willie, you're taking the micky again. Go and put on your suit till I see it."

"Practical Pam, that's my girl!"

3

Aberdeen airport, Dyce, Monday morning 7 am, Willie checked in for his shuttle flight to Heathrow, and with four hours to kill before his onward flight to the States he rang a London stockist of Glen Dufftown for a lunchtime appointment, eager to clinch his first order.

The off the peg suit did a good job as Willie smiled at himself while tucking the signed order form into the sleeve of his briefcase and hailing a taxi back to the airport.

"That's six cases, only ninety four to go," thought Willie, as he smiled again.

"You're a happy gent," said the taxi driver. "Have you just had some good news?"

"Yip," smiled Willie. "I've just started my new job and got my first sale. I'm on my way to America to hopefully get more orders. Wish me luck."

"You Jocks don't need an Englishman's luck - you've got the luck of the Irish, just like the Welsh have."

This was Willie's first trip abroad on his own since going to Australia to visit his doctor pals in Sydney, and the freedom from family and restraints of the still was breathing new life into the soul of the man. He felt he was in his element, master of his time, brimming with confidence for the forthcoming American style sales pitch. "I'll get them off their Bourbon, that Tennessee whiskey gut rot and onto Glen Dufftown before they've time to pour their second dram. Glen Dufftown will be known as the scotch of Manhattan, America's favourite tipple, distilled in Scotland. Christ I'm nearly writing an advert here. Now, maybe that's an idea I could work on."

Willie's brain was in top gear, Pam's words "I suppose you were a bit fed up being at the still all day, you needed a change," echoed loud as his New York bound jet soared high over the Atlantic ocean. America was a new world for Willie, and New York was in the forefront of the culture. He loved Canada and the laid back Canadians, but this was downtown New York, street wise and dangerous. A boy from Dufftown could look out of place and be vulnerable to the unscrupulous street con men who cruise the Manhattan walk ways. No matter how good Willie thought his New York accent was, it wouldn't fool the hardened New Jersey wide boys, to whom conning tourists is an art form.

The American whisky market was increasingly buoyant and Willie's quest was really just to expand the number of agents stocking his whisky. The Glen Dufftown raw spirit, which was filled into reconditioned bourbon casks, giving the whisky its distinctive flavour were bought in from America several years before the whisky they matured was bottled, sold and shipped back to the states. Willie's catch phrase during his sales pitch regularly became, 'We'll buy your old barrels, if you buy our new whisky'.

"We're going full capacity at Dufftown just now,

we'll need a phenomenal amount of casks, next close season we're puttin' in two new stills and that will nearly double our output There's a whole world out there just gasping for a sniffter o' oor classic malt."

The Americans loved Willie's persona, lapping up his sales patter, and the orders just rolled into his order book. Selling Glen Dufftown was turning out to be Willie's dream job. He just couldn't fail with the Americans, they loved their malts and Willie was selling the best one. Voted the best Speyside malt for the past five years, was anybody but Willie brave enough to state Glen Dufftown was the best malt whisky in the world? Willie believed it, and his early sales figures were showing that the Americans thought so, too. Made in the world's whisky capital it couldn't be anything else but number one.

'Just imagine,' thought Willie. 'If I sold enough Glen Dufftown to make it the world's best selling malt, what an achievement that would be.

With a full order book, a very happy whisky salesman flew home to the arms of his family and the solitude of his Cabrach castle pondering how surreal it was to be in American cities one day and in the quiet Cabrach the next.

Saturday morning Willie picked up his made to measure suit and splashed out on the pair of Grenson brogues he'd promised himself if his sales trip to America proved fruitful. For Pam, he bought a £50 voucher so that she could treat herself to a nice pair of shoes on her next trip to Elgin. Willie's weekends now were totally free of work related interruptions: while manager he would regularly be called to the still to sort out any production hiccups, but now he could devote all weekend doing family things. Project number one was a play shed for Gary and Amy's bikes and outdoor games. A ten by eight tongue and groove construction with a felt roof on a railway sleeper base was erected with the help of Willie and Pam's dad the following Sunday, replacing the old domed Nissan hut that leaked and was looking its age.

The weekends were short, and in the blink of an eye, after several domestic sales trips, Willie was off again abroad, this time to Europe. France, Spain and Germany were the top whisky drinkers across the channel, but despite his lack of languages Willie wanted to add Italy, Greece, Belgium, and Holland to the list.

Willie flew to Madrid, then backtracked to Barcelona and Paris, meeting the buyers whose orders he hoped would give him a good start in Europe, but he found it was a totally different market place than America, demanding a less flamboyant approach. Almost instantly he realised the language barrier was going to inhibit his sales in Europe.

'The sooner I'm selling to more English speaking countries the better,' he thought. 'I hope the French and Germans are easier to deal with than these Spanish, then there's the Italians and Greeks next week. I'll never reach my targets without selling to more English speaking countries. I wonder if the bosses will allow me a trip to Australia, New Zealand and Canada?'

Willie pulled back from trying to oversell to the Europeans and left them to place their own orders direct to Glen Dufftown's distribution offices in Glasgow when they saw fit.

Back home, Willie settled down on the couch with Pam mid evening Saturday to discuss a two week sales stint away from the family, and to see if she would teach him some basic French.

"I never thought of that before Willie, you not speaking another language. I'd forgotten you went straight to the still from school at fifteen."

"Well fa' needs languages at a still Pam? Whisky's the same in any language."

"The guides need to speak another language," explained Pam. "The new generation of guides. Once the old foggies have retired, new guides will only get a job if they speak French, German, Italian or Spanish, so you would do well to get crackin' and parle vous francais? Just a small amount of French will see you a long way to getting by on your next trip."

"Cie vous ples! When do we get started?"

It was immediately planned that every evening for the following two weeks would be devoted to Willie's crash course in French - with no respite.

"We start right now, Willie. First question in English, 'How many cases would you like?' Now in French, 'Vous voulez combien de caisses?'"

"Next question, 'Would you like mixed cases of twelve, twenty, twenty five years? Now the French pronunciation Willie: 'Vous voulez un melange du 12, du 20 et 25 ans d age?' Now lets repeat those two questions and practice them."

Willie wrote them down and promised Pam he'd practice them on the plane to France.

"Okay," said Pam, who proceeded with the next question, "How about a couple of cases of our new Seven Hills Liquor? 'Et pour quoi pas deux caisses de notre nouvelle liqueur Seven Hills'. Your customers will ask when will they get their orders, so we better do that one Willie." Willie at this point was beginning to fade, but knew he had to hold on for a few more minutes. " 'Quels sont vos delais de livraison'?"

"Pam, that's great! Can I pour a dram now for us? We've worked so hard. French is easy for them French but hell for us Scots."

"Willie, it'll all fall into place as long as you practice," said a confident Pamela.

4

The sharp frosts of late autumn were descending on Speyside as Willie rehearsed the few French phrases he'd learned from Pam. A pre-Christmas sales trip to Europe beckoned, and Willie would have to be at his ambassadorial best to clinch the crucial bumper sales. His timing had to be pretty accurate: too early and the agents wouldn't be ready to place their orders, too late and they'd have placed their orders with some other malted brand.

This was by far Willie's busiest time of year, a clean sweep of the European countries, two cities a day, check in, sleep, check out, get the sale, check in, sleep, check out, get the sale... And after two full-on weeks, Willie flew home from Rome utterly exhausted, and was more than glad of the following three days off before going into his office to process the entries in his bulging order book.

In record time, Willie had his spate of Christmas orders crated, labeled and loaded onto the Glen Dufftown artic bound for the continent. The next few weeks leading up to Christmas Willie spent going round his local customers making sure they were well stocked for the rush of shoppers looking for that extra special bottle of malt to caress the palates of their whisky loving friends.

5

A flurry of snow greeted the Thompson family as they awoke to a Cabrach Christmas day that seemed in the middle of the night for Pam and Willie. Like all children the world over, the excitement of 'I wonder what Santa has brought me' rouses them, bright as buttons, at five am, and within the hour every livingroom in the country is awash with toys, wrapping paper and cardboard boxes. In some households, even the family pet gets a tin of their favourite food wrapped up in a pretty parcel.

As the Christmas morning hours ascended towards twelve noon, Willie took Gary and Amy sledging while Pam prepared the Christmas day feast of traditional roast turkey with all the usual trimmings. And as the Queen related her annual message to the nation, the Thompson family tucked in and gorged themselves to oblivion.

In total contrast to Christmas day, Boxing Day morning was a long lingering lie in. The planned trip to Pam's parents to show off the presents had to be put on hold for another day as during the night the weather turned stormy and snow drifts blocked the Cabrach to Dufftown road. Great for the kids sledging, but unadvisable for driving when the journey was not really necessary.

"If we're blocked in, then Cockbridge to Tomintoul's definitely blocked," laughed Willie, looking forward to a chilled out day with a dram in front of his wood burning stove. There was plenty of 'in house' entertainment for Pam and the kids, and lots of Christmas day leftovers to munch on, so everyone was happy to stay home.

The day darkened early with heavy laden snow clouds filling the Cabrach skyline, the only sign of life down both sides of the valley was the intermittent drifting smoke plumes from croft house chimneys. The area's wildlife were well accustomed to the harshness of their environment, leaving only their footprints in the virgin snows as proof of their existence. Local farmer George Robertson cleared the road past Willie and Pam's with his home built snowplough, but it would only take a few hours to fill in again and by daybreak the following morning, no trace of snow clearance would be left visible.

CHAPTER ELEVEN

THE HAGGIS HUNT

1

To help shorten the Cabrach winter, and in other glens of Scotland, on the tenth of January each year before the official shooting season opens, a special licence is given to land owners to hunt the haggis, Scotland's own bird of paradise. Fifteen days before poet Robert Burns' birthday, the heather moors of Scotland are swarming with hoards of 'heather beaters', who noisily beat the heather moor land trying to dislodge the haggi from their hiding hole, forcing them to fly forward to the waiting Barber jacketed and green wellied brigade, who take great joy from gunning them down.

The first day of the season's hunt gets under way with an early start as the guns (toffs who enjoy the sport), and beaters gather around 7 am in the courtyard of the estate pile. It would be the only time during the hunt that the two classes (toffs and commoners) would be seen to mingle. As a teenager, Willie was a beater on several haggis hunts, but with Glen Dufftown sponsoring this year's hunt, Willie was in charge of making sure the guns hip flasks were never empty. A fleet of long base Land Rovers with engines purring awaited their green clad passengers, as Spaniel, Labrador, and Retriever dogs ferociously wagged their tails in anticipation of the exciting day ahead. Trained to perfection, these affectionate dogs usually have Scottish names such as Hector, Angus, Baxter and Glen. When a shot haggis falls out of the sky like a lump of lead, the dogs rush to retrieve the haggis for the shooter on the first command, and he who has shot the most haggi at the end of the day is entitled to a double helping of the traditional dish of haggis, neeps, and tatties, and a large dram of Glen Dufftown malt.

Being staunch vegetarians, some of the beaters refuse to work on Sundays, but ten days of moor land madness usually provides more than enough haggis to fully supper the nation in celebration of the national bard on January the twenty fifth. When surplus haggi are shot in a season, they are plucked, prepared, and transported across the border to be enjoyed by the English. But due to a decline in haggi numbers during recent years, finding an Englishman who has tasted a real haggis is quite a rarity.

2

The decline in natural wild haggi has lead to the opening up of farmed haggis, but like farmed salmon it doesn't have the same earthy natural taste, yet is still popular with the inner city clientele who tend to believe their haggis is a butcher's concoction of ingredients.

With the excesses of Christmas and New Year, the revenue generated from sales to butcher outlets of Scottish moor land haggis is as welcomed as the many thousands of pounds from selling the privilege to the guns to shoot them. Until the opening of the salmon season, the haggis hunt can be some estates' only source of income.

The annual haggis shoot season concludes with a celebration, a kind of hair of the haggis, which for the landowners is just another excuse to carry on from celebrating hogmanay. The haggis hunt shunt takes place in the estate house or shooting lodge, with everyone invited, even the bagpipe player. A feast of roast haggis with all the relevant accompaniments and other traditional Scottish fare adorns a large oak dining table at one end of the lodge. Halfway down one side is the ever busy purpose built tattie box bar, and at the other end, a ceilidh band whip up the crowd into a frenzy until it's a free for all.

The haggis hunt shunt is always held on a Friday night, carrying through to Saturday, and for some diehards into Sunday morning with a goody bag of haggis, neeps and tatties as they leave the lodge. Reminiscent of most Scottish highland wedding guests who are often offered soup and oatcakes on leaving the wedding dance, the shunters get so drunk all they can consider focusing on is the three mile wide path in front of them, in a direction they think is home.

The day prior to the start of the haggis hunt, the estate handyman collects together every available wheelbarrow on the estate, dispatching them at the lodge in handiness for a special unique function. Estate workers who have over-indulged themselves at the punch bowl, get barrowed home, while others just sleep in a barrow until day light creeps over the Convals, and Shanks' pony is fit enough to take them home.

During the next few days, the nation's ovens gently roast the thousands of haggi in good time to accompany the thousands of tons of neeps and tatties at countless Burns' suppers throughout Scotland, favourably washed down with gallons and gallons of Glen Dufftown malt. It has been rumoured for some years that Burns supper clubs have formed in other continents as far afield as Australia, New Zealand, America and Canada. It is a rumour of course denied by Scots all over the world, because the educated Scot knows the haggis is not a migratory bird, and therefore none exist other than on Scottish moors.

3

This was a particularly busy January for Willie, as the following Saturday Glen Dufftown were hosting their own Burns supper in the distillery's visitors' centre. A full a la carte up-market five course bill of fare starting with game terrene and home made chutney, cock a leekie or scotch broth, haggis, neeps and tatties, whisky truffles in liquor sauce, and to finish the feast, a Scottish cheese board comprising of traditional cheddar, caboc, crowdie, stitchell, goats cheese, and griddle oatcakes. At each place setting an Edinburgh crystal whisky tumbler accompanied a miniature of Glen Dufftown which was replenished with every course served, whether the previous one had been drunk or not. All in all it proved to be one of the distilleries best PR exercises with many of the 'high heed yins' needing three or four shouts to be told their taxi was waiting to take them to their hotel, or home.

CHAPTER TWELVE

ON THE BOURBON TRAIL

1

The Cabrach winter dragged on through February and into March with a few school days (much to the children's delight) lost to the adverse weather. But, come April it was time for Willie to be off on an American sales trip - to the more Southern States this time, the heart of Bourbon country. Taking Scottish whisky right to the heart of the Bourbon belt was an exciting prospect for Willie. Whisky salesmen had tried before and failed but that to Willie was what made it more of a worthwhile challenge. All the Southern states would get the call from the malt whisky maker.

Being a lover of the cowboy lifestyle, Willie's Southern States itinerary started in Nashville moving down the Mississippi highway to Memphis and New Orleans. Willie was a piper but loved country rock and Nashville was country's holy grail, although the country music of the eighties was more West coast America. Cowboy boots, Stetson and malt whisky,

"If I could strum a few guitar chords together I'd write

a country song about whisky," mused Willie. "How cool would that be? 'I've spilt my malt whisky all over the range, should've bin over the dog cos he's got the mange, Whisky o' whisky I wish that, you overflowed from my ten gallon hat'." If it's country, don't sing the blues.

With his cowboy genes fully liberated, Willie headed for Memphis with more malt whisky inside him than he'd sold to the cowboys of Nashville. As he drove South thinking. 'I better get my act together in Elvis's town or the bosses back home won't be happy. Maybe we should do a commemorative bottle on the year of Elvis's death, or one to commemorate all his number ones, and as he has Scottish ancestry from Aberdeenshire, I think it's a damn good idea, I better note that down for when I'm back home.'

2

As Willie rolled into Memphis in his hired Chevy, discarding his Stetson and cowboy boots for brogues and pinstripe suit, he immediately went to work at the first liquor store he came across in town.

"Hi there, may I introduce myself, I'm Willie Thompson, a whisky salesman from Scotland, can I interest you in malt whisky? Do you think there would be a market in the Southern States?"

"That's a tough call, Scotsman. This is Bourbon country, we just like 'Tennessee whiskey' here. You need to be selling to the yanks up North."

"Yeah, well, I'm just trying to spread the word of Scotch a bit wider, but maybe I'm floggin' a dead horse in these parts."

"You may get a few sales in New Orleans, it's a

more cosmopolitan city, plenty tourists who like the jazz, and blues scene."

"What about all the Elvis lovers who come to worship at Graceland? Do you think there would be an opening there?" asked Willie.

"You could certainly try, but I don't think you'll have much success," said the liquor store owner. "That's pretty much a closed shop. If it doesn't have Elvis's name on it they won't take it."

"Well, I might as well give it a go anyway. I'm on Elvis's doorstep so I should do the Graceland tour at least before trying my luck in New Orleans. Love him or hate him Elvis was an originator, he's maybe been dead for twelve years but he still brings huge revenue to the Memphis economy."

"Don't leave town without visiting his shrine at Graceland."

The liquor store owner's words echoed loud as Willie felt more a pilgrim of rock an' roll than a whisky salesman, parking his Chevy in the massive Graceland car park. As he walked up the steps of Graceland he got the feeling that business was not going to mix with pleasure and went ahead and did the Elvis devotee tour. At first, Willie paid no attention to the tour guide as she led the disciples from room to room, but as he began to relax and let the moment wash over him, the tone of her voice, cut of her skirt, and wry smile was making an impression on the Dufftown loon.

For the first time since wooing Pam, a face, figure and smile of a Southern Belle was getting Willie excited in the nether regions. Without giving home and family a thought Willie wanted to talk to the slinky chocolate coloured guide, following her every word on the king's career, and was ready to pounce as soon as she concluded her tour.

"You have to be a devoted Elvis fan, and dedicated to your job to give a tour like that," said the silver tongued Dufftownite, hoping for a quick reply.

"I do alright I suppose, but it's pretty easy when you've done it every day for five years, and really the people who come to Graceland simply worship Elvis, so as long as you say nice stuff about him they leave happy."

Willie was smitten and desperate to date the damsel of Graceland. He'd sold no whisky but he needed to celebrate anyway. "Can I take you to dinner? I'm eager to try Southern cuisine and I'd love you to join me."

"I'd love to, and I know exactly where to go for the best at a reasonable price."

"Well I need to get booked into a hotel, but can I meet you at seven downtown?"

"Well if you let me know your name I'll come to your hotel and we'll go to the restaurant together."

"That's a good idea. If you know my name and I know yours, that's a good start. Willie Thompson, Scottish and proud, now your turn."

"Willie, pleased to meet you, I'm Corrina Johnson, Memphis born an' bred. My dad was from up around the lakes, my mum still stays pretty close and I see her every once in a while. So what brings you to Memphis, you don't seem like an Elvis fan?"

"Well, to tell you the truth I'm a whisky salesman, Scottish whisky."

"Willie we're Bourbon drinkers down here. You should be up in the Northern states. It's the city slickers that drink your whisky."

"Well I just thought I'd sell some of my malt here in the Southern states, but it looks like I'm nae gonna."

Thousands of miles from home Willie had no guilty conscience and Corrina was every part the woman he desired. He could resist everything but temptation and their equal love of red wine gave the opportunity for them to be intimate with each other. Kissing in the balmy Southern air led to 'my place or yours' and passionate love making which both participants were equally eager to pursue further. This was more than one night stand material, something in the chemistry demanded more.

3

Still with no sales, Willie was getting desperate to be on his road to New Orleans. If he could get an order for a few cases his trip would pay for itself and the bosses might not be on his back when he returned home. Flying to New Orleans was the only option, get a quick sale and be back in Memphis the same night to see Corrina.

Heading for the French quarter straight from the airport, Willie secured a sale in a part of town where blues, jazz and malt whisky gyrate together like peas in the pod of life. By 6 pm Willie was back in Memphis phoning Corrina to meet up and chew at the stick of romance for what he thought it was worth.

As Friday approached it suddenly dawned on Willie he was close to catching a plane home to Scotland, and his Southern American romance, brief but full on, would be erased and gone forever. Could a seventy two hour fling on another continent be anything more?

"One last dinner date and then it's the parting of the

ways," he kept repeating to himself as he drove to pick up Corrina at her town house. "Hell, I feel so guilty. This just isn't me, but God I couldn't resist her, the attraction was so electric!" And as Corrina opened her front door to Willie, all adulterous thoughts disappeared in a passionate bear hug-like clinch. They couldn't resist each other, and by the time they reached Corrina's bedroom both were semi-naked and hotter than the brownest smuggled Speyside whisky.

With all their sexual tensions addressed and satisfied, their dinner date resumed at a small nearby restaurant with fulfilling conversation and laughter. They were having a wonderful time and thoroughly enjoying each other's company, swapping stories alternatively. Corrina would relate her tales of unusual Elvis fans on her Graceland tour, and Willie told his latest whisky smuggling story.

"Just while I was leaving the distillery to come on this trip, the guys were speaking about a story they'd heard that was pretty funny. Do you want to hear it?"

"Of course, Willie, I like all your stories."

"Well if you are sitting comfortably, I will begin... It was the last filling of whisky before close season - that's when the distillery closes down for summer maintenance - and the usual procedure after all the jobs were done was to empty any spirit collected in the filling head pale out onto the concrete floor where it would evaporate. But the filling head had leaked about half a pailful and the filling store man thought, 'I'm nae throwin' away that much whisky!' And, wondered how he could get it out of the distillery and safely home. After a few minutes of serious deliberation with himself, he came up with the idea. 'If I drain out the window washer reservoir in my car, I'll get the spirit in there'."

"An inspired idea," said Corrina.

Willie continued: "So with a window washer full of raw whisky spirit, the filling store man drove home undeterred. As it was close season the filling store man and family had planned a driving holiday to France, so next morning with their car loaded with luggage they set off for the continent. With all the holiday talk and preparations to consider when getting home from work he completely forgot about the reservoir of whisky, and it only re-entered his head as they approached customs on arrival in France. 'Oh shit the whisky', he cries. Oblivious to the reason for her husband's outburst, his wife just thought he'd forgot to stop at the duty free for a bottle of whisky. Nothing else was said until several miles from the ferry terminal, he stopped the car to explain his outburst. 'You'll never believe it, but I smuggled whisky out of the distillery, and I smuggled it into France'. 'What', said his wife, 'where is it?' 'In the window washer reservoir'. 'Well, thank God it didna' rain on the way here'. 'Well, if it had we would've had a really clean windscreen', said the filling store man, and the whole family had a good laugh."

The filling store man's story, Willie felt. would've been funnier with a whisky crowd on Speyside, but as he'd ordered up his and Corrina's third bottle of red wine, the laughter was in full flow anyway. Across the dining table Willie gazed into Corrina's almond coloured eyes and knew in another time this would've been the perfect love match, but at home three thousand miles away a loving wife and family were awaiting a husband and father in the next twenty four hours whose thoughts should only be for them.

Fired up by the wine's alcohol, Willie and Corrina were laughing at the silliest of comments and looking desperate to leave the restaurant before ravaging each other over the table. Luckily for the restaurant's other customers, they contained their lust and passion for each other until outside on the short walk back to Corrina's flat. A mid morning flight would take Willie to New York and onto London for his teatime domestic flight to Aberdeen, and back home to his family, but for tonight the love struck couple had only their own lusty needs in mind.

4

Reporting in to work with only an order for one case of twelve year old malt on Monday morning, Willie knew it was unlikely the bosses would let him return to the Southern States on another sales trip, making him feel less guilty about his romantic misdemeanour.

"I suppose we were hoping for a little too much down in the Southern states. We just felt we had a good man on the job, but it's obviously a tough go," said Willie's boss. "You'd better be off to the guaranteed sales grounds next week so we can keep this ship afloat."

'If he only knew the half of it,' thought Willie. 'The Southern States might be poor for whisky sales, but wonderfully fruitful for romance.'

"Willie," said his boss. "We were thinking it's time for Glen Dufftown to be looking at the more provincial towns of North America. The big city agents are well established, and as you've been across to introduce yourself we feel we need to be selling further afield."

Willie reached for the American map. "I'll start with Boston and take it from there. Ottawa, Toronto, Buffalo maybe, there's plenty Scots in that corner." The bosses then left for a two-hour lunch, leaving Willie to book himself into a downtown Boston hotel for the following Monday night.

'If I secure one agent in each city surely that will redeem me from my Southern States disaster', thought a confident Willie.

5

Boston was blustery, with heavy rain showers coming in from the Atlantic coast.

"This weather's the same as Dufftown's," said Willie, pulling up the collar of his Johnston's of Elgin cashmere coat while paying his taxi driver.

"Where's Dufftown," asked the taxi man.

"Dufftown, my good man, is in the heart of whisky country in Scotland."

"I guessed you were Scottish, but I've never heard of Dufftown."

"Well it's in the North East of Scotland, just like Boston's in the North east of America."

"Tell me," says Willie, "where in Boston is the best place to buy whisky?"

"Didn't ya take some with ye if you're from Scotland?"

"Well I've got some miniatures, here's one for you."

"Gee, that is decent of you, thanks, and mind how you go now Scotsman."

"Ah well," sighed Willie, "America, here we go again! I wonder what delights await me this time."

"I'll get that sir!" And before Willie could say "What?" his case had been snatched from his side and was at the hotel desk awaiting a room number. "Just follow on when you're ready, sir," said a breezy porter.

Willie was back in the fast, slick America, not the slow laid back marshes of the South. "This is the 'have a nice day, sir' America that I'm used to," he smiled to himself as he quickened his step for the lift. "A concierge, room service, a mini bar, and colour telly in my room. It's hard to be humble in such opulence. I wonder what the poor people are doing now? All I need now is Boston's 'More than a feeling' and my first night in Boston would be perfect."

Never content to fully enjoy the moment, Willie lay back on his Boston hotel bed hankering over a trip to the Far East, but because of his disastrous sales figures in Mississippi he thought he'd better let the dust settle for six months or so before mentioning it to his bosses.

"If I produce sales figures to please the suits, I could get a New Zealand and Aussie trip. Sell whisky, see the world."

Seeing the world might have been an overstatement from Willie. Sure, he flew to lots of countries and visited their cities, but his time was spent selling cases of whisky rather than sight seeing, and Boston was no exception. Willie was up next morning ready to do six to seven hours of promotion and hopefully sales, before flying across the Canadian border to Ottawa, Canada's capital.

The moment he set foot in Ottawa, he phoned his bagpipe-playing pal Rob in Toronto, to see if he was up for a drink the following night.

"Willie Thompson from Dufftown, get here early, I haven't seen you for years, we've got to catch up," said an excited Rob, who was as laid back a Canadian as Willie had ever met, but got excited if there might be a party in the offing. "How's Pamela and the kids? Remind me, what's their names? And how's Dufftown? Gee I loved that town."

"Gary and Amy," Willie got their names in edgeways but it was to deaf ears, Rob was far too excited about the visit from his Scottish pal, and what kind of evening they might have downtown Toronto, to care about registering children's names.

"Rob are you still working with Canadian Club? When Pam an' me were here last time you were hopin' to get the area manager's job."

"Yip that's me. Rob McKinnon, area manager. My area covers six states: three in Canada, three in America."

"Brilliant Rob, but I hope your Club drinkers are also whisky drinkers," said Willie, only half joking.

"Willie, we'll have a good time tonight, then tomorrow I'll introduce you to a couple of my best customers here in town."

"How about a couple of good leads in some other cities Rob? I really need to pull off some bumper sales on this trip to redeem my soul."

"Stay two nights, Willie, and you'll be going home with all the leads you need, and all it'll cost you is a bed for me on my holidays to Dufftown."

"Are you still leading the bachelor life, or are you hiding the wife and kids at your country retreat, Rob?"

"Still single, Willie. For a few years yet, I think. My romantic rendezvous all seem to end in a romanticised mess. Maybe I should move to the West Coast for the Californian girls, blonde and bronzed with bodies to die for. We need to eat Willie, will we call in a pizza or do you want to dine out?"

"Well, I'd rather dine out, hang the expense, it's on me. Somewhere middle priced that's not too classy."

"I know the exact venue for us, Willie. There's a diner just off the Ontario highway serves the best steak around, and at Dufftown prices too!"

6

Steaks the size of barn doors on ashets the size of flying saucers washed down by ample bottles of beer and then the boys were off downtown to sample the Toronto nightlife, that Willie thought would be like any other modern cosmopolitan city. Flashing neon lights outside with deafening loud music inside, but downtown Toronto he quickly realised was no Manhattan.

"Dufftown on any Saturday night is livelier," said Willie offering his opinion to Rob as they moved onto their next beer stop. Toronto bars were more sedated than the hedonistic clubs of Europe, offering a more relaxed atmosphere, but perhaps disappointing for two males in their early forties who were in search of their long departed youth. Another bar, another beer, and to liven up their evening and be a bit radical. the pals decided to alternatively drink a malt whisky and a Canadian club spiked by American dry ginger. Willie wanted a dram, Scottish style, Rob wanted a shot, Canadian style. To compromise they invented the 'Canada Maccan' and proceeded to get thoroughly inebriated.

7

Waking up at noon next day, wondering how they made it

back to the flat apparently unscathed, a hangover cure was desperately needed to start their day, a day when Rob promised Willie some heavy weight introductions.

"Hung over or not, Rob, I need these intros. Let's catch breakfast on the way to the first."

Showered and shaved, the duo headed out suitably attired like the hardened salesmen they were. Rob's introductions got Willie off to a great start in his Toronto sales. It was as if the whisky stockists were just waiting on his arrival through their shop doors, Willie's order book was again showing signs of bulging in the corners.

As the two salesmen were on a high, Rob took the opportunity of accompanying Willie on a short flight to Buffalo to cast his own sales net around some customers he hadn't visited all year. Weary from their previous night's partying the pals booked their hotel rooms and had an early night.

Next morning, two introductions in Buffalo and two sales/ "It's never been this easy, Rob. Every time I come to Canada and this East neuk of America, you have to be with me on the rounds, we're just an unstoppable force!"

"Anytime, Willie. Selling is just such great fun."

An airport lounge bar beer, and their flights in opposite directions were ready to board.

"Don't be too long in coming to Dufftown, Rob, it'll be great to see you anytime, just give me a ring," shouted Willie as he entered the departure lounge for his New York flight, en route to Heathrow and home.

8

Spring had blossomed in the Dufftown countryside during

Willie's two American sales trips, and he was glad to be on home soil during his favourite season of the Scottish year. The three semi matured cherry trees he and Pam planted the previous autumn were in full bloom at the far end of their lawn, blending well with the deep green of the conifers that lined the garden fence.

Willie's only bugbear about spring was getting the lawn mower out of its winter hibernation to keep the grass at a respectable and manageable length, It was the only housekeeping chore he disliked, but now and again he managed to tempt his father with the odd bottle of whisky, and miraculously when Willie got home from work, he was greeted by a well shorn lawn. The garden at Cabrach Castle was now well established, demanding attention weekly, and when returning from his globetrotting the last thing Willie wanted to do was keep a tidy garden.

"It's good of your dad to cut the grass, Willie, but you can't expect him to do it all. We need to get a part time gardener."

"You're right, Pam. Although dad enjoys his day up here, he's got a fair sized garden of his own to keep, but there's a guy I know in Rothes who does gerdens, I'll gie him a ring, his name funnily enough is Charlie Gardener, pass me the phone book till I get his number."

9

The school summer holidays were only weeks away, Pam and Willie had talked about a family holiday but had not decided where. With going abroad so often in his job, Willie wanted a holiday of complete contrast with no airports in sight. Luckily for Willie, Pam too was of the same opinion.

And if the kids agreed to a week's camping and a week at a loch side chalet complex, then they would have their holiday without too much travelling.

As Willie was now not directly involved with production at Glen Dufftown, he could take his summer holidays when he wished, not waiting for close season. And with Charlie the gardener keeping the garden duties ship shape, it gave Willie and Pam time together to discuss holidays, Willie's free time for relaxing, and playing with his children when he got home from work.

Charlie Gardener had twenty years behind him in part time gardening, but his main job was as a still man working on shifts at Ben Aigan distillery, Rothes. He was forty something, stuck in the seventies, still wearing Wrangler flaired denims, and black leather pleated jacket on a rare Saturday night out in the Rothes night spots. Leisure hours to Charlie was waisted time, but to keep on the regular side of sanity he felt it was important he be seen out on a Saturday night nursing a pint of beer. It was comforting for the other pub regulars to ask, 'Has Charlie been in?' rather than silently wonder, 'Is that eccentric guy who does the gerdens okay?' Still fit and athletic, Charlie kept in good shape, bolstered by his endless calorie burning, and despite his apparent glaiketness, a certain charm shone through.

Eighties' night life in small Speyside towns was enjoyable, older members of the communities engaged themselves in conversation with the towns' youth as they moved from pub to pub in search of an evening of fun in their town. The town they were born in, brought up in, went to school in, worked in, and played in (perhaps even rumblin' spoots!?) on a Saturday night. Their town roots were planted years ago, and most had no intentions of ever derooting, they were comfortable with the town they knew, their universe was intact.

Before his two to ten shift, Charlie would arrive at the Thompsons for eight sharp, to get in four hours gardening before his shift, and when on six to two he'd arrive at three and work till seven. Such dedication to working can only be admired. The days that Willie glanced Charlie working in his garden he would take a moment to humble himself and remember the days when he'd go straight to bed for a snooze when he finished his shift. Some people are born to work, and work hard, others, like Willie, work smarter, and are in jobs that seem like paid hobbies. When Willie was a shift worker he was always checking his watch, hoping for the magic hour when he'd get home for a sleep. Charlie was a grafter and at his happiest when at work, whether in gardens or at the still it didn't matter, as long as it was work.

Charlie kept the Thompson garden pristine throughout the summer months of constant growth, becoming a trusted friend by all the family. As Willie was hardly ever around with his work commitments at home and abroad, it was down to Pam to pay Charlie. Bachelor Charlie was hardly a lady magnet, but somehow a certain chemistry seem to bubble between him and Pam. Charlie's coffee breaks were getting longer, the chit chats with Pam were getting more flirty, they were both in danger of crossing that fine line of deceit.

Although Charlie was in good shape, he was certainly no Robert Redford, finding charisma of that calibre in the Cabrach was pretty rare, but if the mercury is rising, it's hard to ignore it no matter who you are. Charlie's charisma was a little more difficult to detect than Robert Redford's, but it was definitely there, embedded deep down somewhere in his Scottish psyche. There wasn't much call for charisma in his distillery job or folk's gardens, so it was something he'd never thought about. Charming Pam into bed had really nothing to do with him, he just happened to be available and willing, being a confirmed bachelor with the odd romantic liaison was a world he was comfortable and happy in. Short on witty, stimulating conversation was no drawback for Charlie, as he grew the best cabbages in Banffshire.

With Willie on the other side of the world, no noisy neighbours, the kids at school, and hardly any passing traffic who was going to catch them.

'Who's to say?' thought Pam, 'When Willie's abroad is *he* behaving himself?

"It's only a fling, Charlie, don't go thinking there's a future in this, I just get a little lonely sometimes when Willie's away, and if any weeds appear in the garden he'll get suspicious, so we can't lie in this bed of passion and sin too long."

"I fancied you, Pam, the first day I came to cut the grass when you were hanging out the washing, and the way you smiled I thought you weren't one hundred per cent happy."

"Well, I hope I don't look too sad and depressed, it's just now and again I kinda lose my momentum. Charlie, you always seem happy, yet you're never stopped working."

"When I'm not working, Pam, I'm bored. And if I get bored, I get down."

"What, you get down and boogie?"

"Pam, it's that sense of humour that's so attractive. I wish I was funny like that. Probably it's because I work all the time that I'm so dull. A dull but happy Charlie."

"You're not dull, Charlie. Well, certainly not at being passionate anyway!"

The illicit lovers kissed and cuddled the morning into afternoon till Charlie left to start his two to ten shift at Ben Aigen.

10

The illicit love affair was to be short lived as Pam was getting too panicky to let it continue into another month. Both Pam and Charlie agreed he should stop as gardener at the Cabrach castle, giving Willie the excuse he'd picked up two other gardens in Rothes, which was better economics than travelling to the Cabrach twice a week. True or not, every travelled mile was a pound lost as far as Charlie was concerned, even with just one garden job on his doorstep, he was quids in.

Despite the nervousness she felt with her adulteress misdemeanour, it only took Pam a couple of days to put the liaison behind her. She wasn't the first lonely housewife to have an affair with her gardener, and certainly wouldn't be the last. Pam still had ten days to build up her cool persona before Willie returned home from his current sales trip. Never one to be smothering his family with long distance telephone calls, he preferred to wait until he was home at weekends to catch up with all the local gossip, so Pam had time on her side to conjure up any story she wished, should she need to defuse any inkling of mistrust.

A pensive Willie arrived home clutching the latest copy of the whisky world's ultra glossy monthly magazine. Unhappy at the content of the main news article he quickly poured an adequate dram, commenting to Pam, "What are we going to do? Blended whisky sales are stagnant!"

"Well," said Pam, "if blended whisky is in decline, you'll need to concentrate more on expanding the sales of malt whisky."

"Pam, that's brilliant, I think you've hit the nail on the head, we should be catering more for the whisky connoisseur and not chase the Saturday night binge market. Monday morning I'll mention it to the boss, and you, Pam, will get a thirty year old for your brainwave."

"Yeah, but better say it's your brainwave! It'll carry more weight at board level, but I'll still take the whisky."

With his head in the clouds, a bee in his bonnet, excitement and anticipation in control, he was in a right raid up, Willie raced into his office on Monday morning eager to air his views on marketing Glen Dufftown malt in all sorts of combinations of years and presentations.

He thought: 'I better tell Bob the manager before I phone head office with Pam's brainwave'.

"Bob, how do you feel about exploiting the malts?"

"Exploit them by drinkin' them Willie?"

"No, Bob, by selling them, presenting them as collectors' items at hugely inflated prices. The blended market is ticking over, holding its own, but I think there's a great future in collectors' edition malts."

A board meeting was arranged for Willie to travel to the companies Glasgow headquarters on Thursday at which Willie displayed drawings to emphasise his marketing of the malts. So impressed were the company owners with Willie's enthusiasm and obvious commitment to pure malts that they excused him from the meeting to discuss the possibilities of offering Willie the position of sales and marketing director for the company. As Willie hovered in the corridor of power sipping a black coffee and thinking:'Shit, I've overdone it this time! They're gonna send me home with my tail between my legs. Maybe I haven't thought this through right, but it's whisky - what more needs to be thought out?'

The board room door opened and a less confident Willie walked round the board table to his original seat.

"Well, Willie we have had a short but comprehensive discussion on your presentation and we think it's a wonderful idea. We wish to offer you promotion onto the board as director for sales and marketing. Don't give us an answer just now, Willie, but if you do accept the position, can we call you Bill? We just think Bill is more a boardroom name."

Willie was blown sideways, being brand ambassador was honour enough, but to join the board of directors was far beyond any achievement he'd dreamed of. When he got his breath back, he thanked them all, and steamed off up the A9 for home to delight his family with the exciting news.

"Pam, I'm home with news you just won't believe! Guess what promotion I got today? They've only gone and asked me if I want to be director of sales and marketing."

"Willie, that's fantastic! Gary, Amy, did you hear that? Your dad's a director."

After the evening family meal, Willie poured a Glen Dufftown from his favourite decanter and sat looking out over Upper Cabrach Croft to the Buck beyond. In the dusky light he was sure he could see a plume of smoke drifting steadily skyward, and as he sipped his fifteen year old he could hear his granddad saying, "Aye, ye'll dee a'right at the whisky, Willie. Ye dinna ken how high you can fly when you participate in the water o' life."

The Life and Times of Willie Whisky is dedicated to the makers of Scottish malt whisky and to the connoisseurs all over the world who enjoy drinking it.
Slaandjivaa

www.kengrantbooks.co.uk